# COLOUR ME BEAUTIFUL
# ·MAKE-UP·
# BOOK

COLOUR ME BEAUTIFUL

# MAKE-UP

## BOOK

### CAROLE JACKSON

PIATKUS

**Also by Carole Jackson**

COLOUR ME BEAUTIFUL
COLOUR FOR MEN

Copyright © 1987 Carole Jackson

First published in Great Britain in 1988 by
Judy Piatkus (Publishers) Limited,
5 Windmill Street, London W1P 1HF
Reprinted 1989 , 1991

British Library Cataloguing in Publication Data

Jackson, Carole, *1942–*
    Colour me beautiful make-up book.
    1. Women. Beauty care – Manuals
    I. Title
    646.7′2′088042

    ISBN 0–86188–777–8
    ISBN 0–86188–872–3 (Pbk)

Designed by Paul Saunders
Illustrations © Marika Hahn
Photography © Michael Latil Photography

Phototypeset in 11/13 Linotron Palatino by
Phoenix Photosetting, Chatham, Kent
Printed in Great Britain by
Eagle Colourbooks Ltd, Blantyre, Glasgow

This book is dedicated to my Colour Me Beautiful
consultants worldwide, whose caring
attitudes and dedication to excellence have
given life to our company and enabled
us to carry out our mission.

## *COLOUR ME BEAUTIFUL PHILOSOPHY*

Colour Me Beautiful believes . . .

- Colours give expression to individual personality

- Colours create a unique sense of pride, well-being, and security

- Colours influence mood, sensitivity, and attractiveness

- Colours accent an individual's best features

- Colours define a person's taste to others

- Colours are enhancements that do not depend on a person's budget

- Colours influence career, love, and life-style

We at Colour Me Beautiful have an opportunity to profoundly change the lives of others for the better.

Our work is therefore more than just a job – it is a calling.

We are in business to be of service to others. Therefore, our mission can only be fulfilled if we are motivated by a sincere and loving concern for others.

This concern must permeate all our thoughts and actions.

# CONTENTS

# THE COLOUR REVOLUTION

When I wrote *Colour Me Beautiful* in 1979 I had no idea so many people would buy it. But now, almost 4 million copies later, I know that millions of women needed (as I did) a sensible system for looking great and for putting together a workable, coordinated and exciting wardrobe.

It started with a simple idea – that we all have special colours that make us look and feel terrific, colours that are grouped for easy reference into four palettes, based on the seasons of nature. The Winter woman looks great in black and white and bright primary colours, the sharp contrast of wintertime. Autumn wears the earth tones best; Summer, the soft whites, blues, and blue-greens of a summer day; and Spring, the fresh new colours of a spring garden.

Less than ten years ago, I was refining the Colour Me Beautiful system in the basement of my house with neighbourhood teenagers assembling our colour swatches by hand. Today, there are Colour Me Beautiful consultants all over the United States, Britain and in twenty-nine other countries, and the book has been published in seventeen languages. Colour Me Beautiful has become a household name. Why? Because the system works! We have now branched out from colour and image consultations and even have our own line of cosmetics and select accessories.

And it's in large part because of you. *You* carried your colour swatches shopping and insisted on buying *your* colours.

Today, in the States, stores, cosmetic companies and manufacturers are using our seasonal colour concept to market their products, which makes shopping easier for everyone. Britain is rapidly following suit, with CMB Colour and Image Seminars being conducted in major department stores and for major companies. Colour Me Beautiful, with your help, is creating change. We've started a colour revolution!

Colour Me Beautiful has been rewarding for me not only professionally, but also in an even more important way. Thousands of women world-wide have written to tell me how finding their colours changed their lives. Some had felt unattractive; some had never had fun with their wardrobe; some had experienced traumatic life changes – the separation or loss of a spouse – or had serious illnesses or accidents and now feel their colours have given them a new lease of life.

It has been thrilling to see the positive impact Colour Me Beautiful has had on so many women. And now I've applied the same principles to make-up, to take away the mystery and show you the magic of colour so you'll look and feel more beautiful than ever.

Carole Jackson
November 1988

*And now it is my pleasure to introduce Mary Spillane, managing director of Colour Me Beautiful, London.*

In Britain it was a slightly different story when we began CMB in 1983. We proceeded with great caution. Would this exciting and unique concept be received favourably by the British, with their high streets full of little but black and grey? Were the British 'anti colour'? Certainly not! You, too, were fascinated to learn that if you dressed in colours that complemented your own natural colouring (skin, eyes and hair), then you looked healthier and more attractive – even younger. Today, we have CMB Image Consultants throughout Britain, offering help to women and men in discovering their best colours and styles and on how to save money when shopping.

Our British success sparked enthusiasm throughout Europe, Africa, and the Middle East, to where we now distribute our famous Seasonal colour swatches, Seasonalised cosmetics and accessories. Over 400 CMB trained consultants offer classes, seminars and products throughout the region.

In Australia and South Africa, where the sun always shines, colour abounds. The streets are now filled with colour-analysed women who are passionate about their Season.

Soon we will see the department stores, cosmetic companies and manufacturers in Britain using the CMB Seasonal Colour Concept to market their products. This will undoubtedly make shopping easier. We know from the letters you send us that you are eagerly awaiting these developments too.

We know you will enjoy this book. In addition, don't forget our consultants are available to show you the magic of colour and to help you to look and feel more beautiful.

Mary C. Spillane
Managing Director, CMB, London

# Part I
# COLOUR ESSENTIALS

# MAKE-UP MAGIC — IT WORKS

We ALL love to see makeovers, don't we? It's intriguing to thumb through a magazine and see a woman with a pale, blotchy face turn into a ravishing beauty on the very same page. And we picture ourselves – in the hands of some fabulous make-up artist – looking gorgeous, too. Or perhaps, just maybe, we could do it ourselves. But how?

I have become more convinced than ever that the majority of women are *intimidated* by make-up. These are the comments I frequently hear:

'Where should I put the blusher?'
'How much should I put on?'
'What colour lipstick should I buy?'
'I don't know how to use a lip pencil.'
'My husband thinks make-up looks unnatural.'
'How do I put on eye make-up?'
'What colour should it be?'
'Won't it make my wrinkles show?'
'Foundation is too thick and gooey – I don't like the way it feels.'
'Powder makes my face look dry and cakey.'

I love answering these questions, working with women, and taking the fear out of wearing and applying make-up.

Growing up in Los Angeles, I was surrounded by movie stars and

Hollywood's emphasis on beauty. Instruction on applying make-up was available for young girls, and when I was fifteen, my mother took me to a make-up salon to learn how to use cosmetics. The make-up artist showed me how to use a lipstick brush to outline my lips and how to put the lipstick on straight. She also mixed some powder for me. For some reason, perhaps because I was so young, I didn't learn about blusher or eye make-up. For several years I wore the lipstick she selected for me (peach – a lovely shade for her colouring, but, alas, not for mine), and I would dot lipstick on my cheeks and blend it with my little finger. In college, I finally discovered powdered blusher, and somewhere along the line I started using eyeliner and mascara, but I didn't use eye shadow until I was almost thirty.

I shudder to think of the colours I used to wear, but today I am an expert on make-up. I came to my expertise through my years of teaching the principles of Colour Me Beautiful, studying with many make-up artists, and experimenting with thousands of women – women with all sizes and shapes of faces and eyes, with young skin and old skin, with complexions and eyes of many different shades.

Most women, I've discovered, have received even less instruction than I did as a young girl. Consequently, many don't wear much make-up, and those who do often apply it incorrectly.

Yet today's women are more up to date than ever. They've read the statistics – women who wear make-up earn 20 per cent more than those who don't. And, in spite of what some men say, make-up, naturally applied, attracts them. What men don't like is make-up that shows or looks garish – which often happens when we wear the wrong colour.

When we were selecting models for the photographs in this book, dozens of 'beautiful' young women appeared with their portfolios. Our young art director was in ecstasy over the gorgeous women we chose. He could hardly wait for the photography shoot so he could gaze at them once more. The morning arrived, and in they came, one after another, each with scraggly straight hair, looking pale and plain with no make-up, wearing jeans and sweatshirts. Robert panicked. 'Where are all the pretty ones?' he whispered. 'Don't worry. They're here,' I replied. Once the make-up artist had worked her magic with the proper colours, her wonderful make-up techniques, and the electric curlers and blow dryer, the beautiful women were indeed there.

We *all* can look beautiful, and no one has to look overly made up to do so. People won't notice your make-up when it is well chosen and properly applied. They will just notice that you are looking better than ever!

When we do a colour analysis, my consultant applies the correct make-up colours to her client's face before 'draping' her with fabric swatches of the clothing colours that look so beautiful on her. Often, the transformation is dramatic. I have watched the right colours transform women from plain to gorgeous in minutes. The right make-up, applied smoothly and naturally, works magic.

Here are some real-life examples:

Maggie left our class – after looking at herself in the mirror many times – grinning from ear to ear. When she got home, her husband kept mentioning how 'happy' and 'radiant' she looked that evening. 'He never even noticed I had on make-up,' she said. 'He just said I looked pretty.' Maggie's husband liked women to look 'natural', so she had never worn make-up before.

Linda's husband had left her. Linda was in her late thirties, one of that generation of women who didn't wear make-up at school or college because it wasn't in vogue. 'Can you believe he left me for an *older* woman?' she said. Linda's morale needed a boost, so we gave her the whole works. She started wearing her colours, got a stylish new haircut, and practised applying make-up until she got it right. She positively sparkled in her salmon pink blusher and lipstick, so perfect for her blonde hair and ivory complexion. Linda soon reported that her social life was terrific, and, more importantly, she was excited about her new life.

Oops. Someone goofed. Wendy had already been colour analysed as a Summer when she came to take our make-up class. As she was applying blusher and lipstick, it rapidly became apparent that the Summer make-up colours did not look good on her. When she switched to an Autumn shade of lipstick, her face came to life. What a difference! The quickest way to select your season is to try on several shades of lipstick. When the colour is *on* your skin, you can immediately see which season's shade is best. Much to Wendy's relief, her Summer wardrobe was not a total loss. Many of the Summer colours she had purchased were similar to Autumn shades – because they were intuitively her favourites. With her new Autumn make-up and a few 'right-colour' scarves, most of her clothing worked.

The story of Mary is one that touches my heart. Mary had lost her grown-up daughter in a car accident and was still severely depressed after a year. On the advice of her counsellor, and in an effort to pull her life together, she came to one of my consultants. My consultant (bless her) had Mary come into her studio almost every day for three weeks to help her with her make-up. Mary had previously worn only lipstick and blusher and had never seen herself looking glamorous before. Gradually, Mary began to think about her own life, and she decided to look for a job that would challenge her. She was hired quickly, and though still grieving, Mary is looking and feeling more beautiful inside and out.

Penny was an extremely attractive woman, already adept at applying make-up. Several weeks after she'd had her colours analysed and had bought her new make-up, she popped in to see us, looking terrific. 'You know, it's just amazing. I remember how I used to feel that my face looked drab, or tired – or something! I'd put on more and more blusher, but it just didn't seem to perk me up. Now I realise it was the wrong colour. I was wearing tawny peach blush and an earthy brown lipstick, and here I am a Winter, needing pinks and fuchsias. No wonder I felt drab. And think of all the money I wasted!'

Brooke never had a date all through school. Her mother brought her to one of our colour-and-make-up classes, where she learned she was a Summer. Brooke skipped foundation because of her youth, but she loved herself in the soft rose blusher and lipstick and the subtle shades of eye shadow she learned to apply. It was inspiring to see how good she felt about herself. She said she had never felt pretty before.

In this book, I will teach you how to choose and apply the perfect make-up for you. In Part I, you'll familiarise yourself with the colour essentials. First you'll find your best colours by taking the Colour Test. Then I'll show you the full range of make-up colours that complement you. Even if you already know your season, and have enjoyed wearing the right colours before, you may not be fully aware of the variety within your make-up colour palette – or how to perfect the harmony of your clothing and make-up combinations. You'll learn to build a 'make-up wardrobe', just as you learned to build a clothing wardrobe in *Colour Me Beautiful*.

In Part II, you'll get a Colour Me Beautiful make-up lesson. I'll lead you step by step through the application of your make-up, just as we do in our Colour Me Beautiful make-up classes, from basic skin care to everyday make-up to make-up for special occasions. We'll keep it simple, so that with a little practice you will feel comfortable and satisfied with your make-up. Once you've mastered the techniques, you will be able to apply your basic, everyday, go-to-work look in about six minutes, or spend perhaps ten or fifteen minutes if you want to do something more elaborate for evening.

Finally, in Part III we'll discuss the finishing touches for your Colour Me Beautiful look: your hair, your nails, and even your scent!

Read the chapters without trying to retain everything. I've summarised all the instructions at the end of the book in a Beauty Workbook you can remove. Place it on your dressing table so you can follow the easy instructions page by page. Once you've applied your make-up a number of times, the routine will become second nature – as easy as brushing your teeth.

I hope you will love this book and keep it next to your copy of *Colour Me Beautiful*. It's not essential that you read *Colour Me Beautiful* before enjoying this book, but if you haven't read it, I suggest you do. It contains a thorough explanation of the colour system and how to determine your personal colours, as well as valuable information on your wardrobe, style, figure, and hair. The principles of the Colour Me Beautiful system are timeless, so nothing you learn from either book will go out of style. You can always adapt a fashion trend to your best look. So enjoy yourself, and have fun looking more beautiful than ever.

CHAPTER · 2

# Colour Me Beautiful:
# THE PALETTES

THE FIRST step in using make-up to your greatest advantage is finding the right colours! The wrong colour on your face can look worse than no make-up at all – and the most expert application in the world cannot compensate for an unflattering colour.

Colour Me Beautiful uses the names of the seasons of nature as a way of describing your colouring and the colours that most flatter you. You are called a Winter, Summer, Autumn, or Spring, depending on the colour of your skin, hair, and eyes. Each season's palette contains its own special array of colours, and *your* colouring is in harmony with *one* of them. Both your make-up and your clothing colours derive from your season's palette.

We all have genetically inherited colouring: skin tone, eye colour, hair colour. Looking around any room full of people you can see the varieties of skin tones. It is impossible for the same shades of make-up to look terrific on all these skin tones. That's why a hot fashion colour can't look good on everyone. We need colours that complement, rather than clash with, our skin.

Winter women look their most beautiful in make-up of sparkling pinks and reds, with cool eye shadows in charcoal, blues, and purples. Their wardrobe colours are the jewel tones and the dramatic black and white of wintertime. Summers are flattered by make-up in soft, gentle pinks, mauves, and watermelons, with eye shadows in hazy grape, aqua, and azure – shades of summer. The Summer woman's wardrobe contains cool, soft colours ranging from pastel pinks and blues to deep, dusty shades of plum, fuchsia, and spruce.

Autumns radiate in rich warm tones. In make-up or wardrobe, their elegance shines in shades of coppery reds, tawny peach, and earthy shades of green, brown, and teal. The Spring woman comes to life in the clear, warm colours of springtime. Her lips delight in coral pinks, peaches, and luscious poppy reds, while her eyes are flattered by soft golden browns, greens, and aquas. Spring's wardrobe contains the colours of a vibrant spring bouquet – yellow, pink, periwinkle blue, coral, and fresh greens.

To determine your best colours, you need to analyse your colouring – your skin, hair, and eyes. If you have already read *Colour Me Beautiful* or have had your colours analysed by a professional colour consultant, then you're familiar with your season's palette. If you don't know your season, you'll have a chance to take the Colour Test in Chapter 3. For now, just look at the colour palettes to familiarise yourself with them. In this chapter, I'll describe the make-up colour palette appropriate for each season and will review the palettes for wardrobe colours.

## *THE SEASONAL PALETTES: MAKE-UP*

Make-up colours come in both *cool* and *warm* shades. Cool shades are ones that have a blue or grey undertone; warm shades have a yellow or golden undertone.

Winter and Summer are the cool seasons. Look at their make-up palettes in the colour section. Notice that the lipstick and blusher colours are in tones of rose, blue-pink, fuchsia, plum, and burgundy. The red lipsticks are bluish, rather than orangish. The eye shadows, too, include cool colours: grey-blues and navies, grape and purple, grey, pink, lavender, mint and spruce green, as well as soft white, greyish browns, and silver. There are no oranges, peaches, or golden colours in the cool make-up palettes. Warm colours will not be flattering on the Winter or Summer woman!

Now study the warm Autumn and Spring palettes on pages 35 and 37. See how these palettes contain warm lipstick and blusher shades of peach, coral, and orange. Here the reds have an orange tone. Even the pinks in the Spring palette are warm pinks – containing yellow. Compare them to the blue-pinks on the Winter and Summer pages.

Notice, too, that the eye shadows consist of tones of peach, gold, golden greens, honey, and coppery browns, as well as copper, bronze, and gold. There are no blue-based colours on the Autumn and Spring charts, for they will be harsh and ageing on a warm skin tone. They will actually clash with your colouring and look unharmonious and unattractive.

In general, when selecting make-up colours your first concern is whether you are warm or cool. Summers and Winters can share some of the same make-up shades, as can Autumns and Springs. Spruce green and cocoa eye shadow, for example, flatter both Winters and Summers, even though the Winter woman wears a brighter pine green or a deep black/brown in clothing. Sage green eye shadow complements both Autumn and Spring eyes, although only Autumn wears it in clothing.

You will undoubtedly notice that a few eye shadow colours show up on all four charts: champagne, aqua, teal blue, teal green, and periwinkle blue. These shades are on the borderline of warm and cool, and will complement both types of skin tone. In addition, you will notice that your make-up choices include colour names that are not on the wardrobe charts. Cosmetic colours blend into your skin and allow you more options.

Next, look at the charts for what I call *value* – how light or dark the colours are. Note that the Winter and Autumn charts contain deeper and brighter colours. Winter and Autumn women, in general, have darker hair and eyes, and need richer colours to offset their colouring. Spring and Summer women often have lighter hair and fairer complexions than their Winter and Autumn counterparts. Their make-up colours will always be lighter, ranging from very soft to medium bright.

Last, note the *clarity* of the colours – whether they are muted down or clear. Both Winter and Spring women look best in make-up colours that are fairly clear and vibrant, even though Winter's are darker than Spring's. See how the lipstick and blusher colours are perky and lively. Spring has many soft shades, but they are clear, not dusty. Autumn and Summer women can wear both clear and muted colours, but are often best in the dusty ones. See how Autumn's red is a brick shade – a muted red. Summer's pink is a dusty rose. Even though all eye shadows have to be somewhat toned down to look natural, you will still find that Summer is best in a greyish grape while Winter chooses a clearer purple. Autumn can wear a smoky turquoise, but Spring needs a clearer aqua.

Your make-up palette contains all the colours you will need to complement the entire spectrum of your season's wardrobe. In addition, the colours in your make-up palette automatically blend beautifully with each other – because they derive from the same cool or warm base. You will delight in the variety of colours and creative combinations in your palette, and in the confidence of knowing that the colours all harmonise with *you*!

## THE SEASONAL PALETTES: WARDROBE REVIEW_____

Like your make-up, your wardrobe palettes also exhibit three distinct qualities: colour (warm or cool), value (light or dark), and clarity (clear or muted).

Look at the colour bars on pages 25, 26, 27, and 28, which depict the wardrobe colours for each season. The Winter and Summer palettes are cool, while Autumn's and Spring's are warm. Note that Winter and Summer both have blue-reds, blue-greens, and blue-based pinks such as fuchsia, magenta, and rose. The Autumn and Spring palettes contain yellow-greens, orange-reds, and golden browns and yellows – all warm colours.

Autumn and Winter colours are again the deepest and most full-bodied, while Summer and Spring have many pastels and light to medium shades. Notice that Winter and Autumn have colours such as black, dark brown, burgundy, mahogany, pine green, forest green, and purple, compared to the powder pink, peach, lavender, sky blue, soft fuchsia, and light orange found in the Summer or Spring palettes.

Last, examine the clarity of the wardrobe colours. The Winter and Spring palettes contain only clear colours; Autumn and Summer colours are more muted.

The following charts list by name the wardrobe colours for each season, in the same order as they appear on the colour bars. You'll find a few new colours, ones that were not included in the original *Colour Me Beautiful* book. Because the colour bars are small, and because printed colour is not as true as coloured fabric, you may want to acquire a set of fabric swatches in your season's wardrobe colour's to use as a shopping guide. The same colours can be used to help select make-up shades. At the back of the book I've included information on how to obtain fabric swatches.

The following pictures show you women of each seasonal type, in right and wrong make-up colours, along with the appropriate make-up palette. You can see how well the correct colours complement the colouring of the models. Once you have determined your colours, you can use your season's make-up chart as a shopping guide. Since cosmetic manufacturers can call a colour anything they want, your colour chart will help you get started. I've given the colours descriptive names to further assist you, as it is difficult to print make-up colours accurately on paper. Don't feel you need to own *all* these colours. Rather, the chart represents your *range* of choices. If you are fair, you'll choose the lighter shades; if your colouring is vivid, you'll wear brighter shades.

The pictures also show you some of the common mistakes women make in applying their make-up so you can see what a difference it makes to place the colours correctly.

The first model – an Autumn (see page 29) – is shown three ways: with no make-up, with minimal make-up, and with complete make-up, adding foundation, powder, and eye make-up. I urge *you* to go for the complete, finished look. A dash of hurriedly applied blusher and lipstick is OK for the tennis court, but for the rest of life it's not enough. Whether at the office, a party, or among friends and family, you're cheating yourself from looking your beautiful best if you don't take the few minutes it requires each morning to achieve a natural but 'complete' look. You'll look more polished, more elegant, more professional, and you'll feel better about yourself, too. You deserve all the compliments that will come your way!

*All colour tints and pictures are subject to the limitations of the printing process.*

# WINTER WARDROBE COLOURS

The Winter woman is best in clear colours and sharp contrast. She wears black and white well and looks great in true, primary colours, royal shades, and ice colours. She avoids golden browns, orange, gold, and dusty pastels.

Neutrals: for coats, suits, jackets, trousers, basic dresses

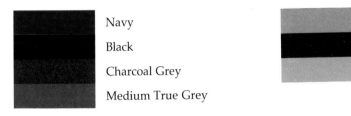

Navy

Black

Charcoal Grey

Medium True Grey

Light True Grey

Black-Brown

Taupe (Grey-Beige)

Lights: for blouses, lingerie, evening wear, warm-weather attire

Pure White

Icy Grey

Icy Blue

Icy Yellow

Icy Pink

Icy Green

Icy Violet

Icy Aqua

Basic and Bright/Accent Colours: for blouses, sweaters, sportswear, dresses (can also be worn in trousers, jackets, and skirts)

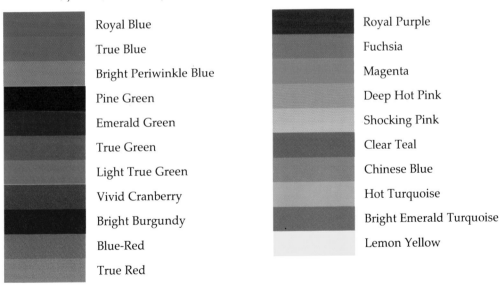

Royal Blue

True Blue

Bright Periwinkle Blue

Pine Green

Emerald Green

True Green

Light True Green

Vivid Cranberry

Bright Burgundy

Blue-Red

True Red

Royal Purple

Fuchsia

Magenta

Deep Hot Pink

Shocking Pink

Clear Teal

Chinese Blue

Hot Turquoise

Bright Emerald Turquoise

Lemon Yellow

*Black-brown, dark periwinkle blue, vivid cranberry, clear teal, and bright emerald turquoise are new additions to the Winter palette.*

## SUMMER WARDROBE COLOURS

The Summer woman thrives on gentle, cool colours, slighly muted, from pastel to deep. She dresses with soft contrast, never sharp or harsh. Summer avoids golden tones, orange, black, stark white, and extremely bright, clear colours.

Neutrals: for coats, suits, jackets, trousers, basic dresses

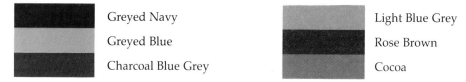

Greyed Navy

Greyed Blue

Charcoal Blue Grey

Light Blue Grey

Rose Brown

Cocoa

Lights: for blouses, lingerie, evening wear, warm-weather attire

Soft White

Rose Beige

Powder Blue

Light Lemon Yellow

Powder Pink

Light Mauve

Lavender

Basic and Bright/Accent Colours: for blouses, sweaters, sportswear, dresses (can also be worn in trousers, jackets, and skirts)

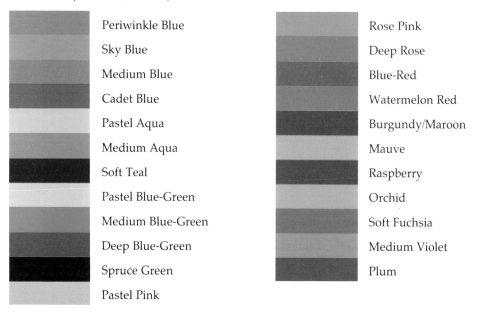

Periwinkle Blue

Sky Blue

Medium Blue

Cadet Blue

Pastel Aqua

Medium Aqua

Soft Teal

Pastel Blue-Green

Medium Blue-Green

Deep Blue-Green

Spruce Green

Pastel Pink

Rose Pink

Deep Rose

Blue-Red

Watermelon Red

Burgundy/Maroon

Mauve

Raspberry

Orchid

Soft Fuchsia

Medium Violet

Plum

*Cadet blue, medium aqua, soft teal, spruce green, and medium violet are new additions to the Summer palette.*

# AUTUMN WARDROBE COLOURS

The Autumn woman looks best in warm, earthy colours, ranging from medium to dark. Her colours must always have a rich quality, even in the lighter shades. She avoids all blue-based colours, fuchsias, blue-pinks, and silvery greys, as well as black and pure white.

Neutrals: for coats, suits, jackets, trousers, basic dresses

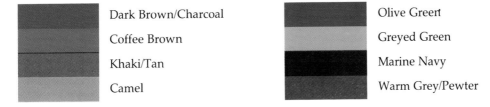

Dark Brown/Charcoal

Coffee Brown

Khaki/Tan

Camel

Olive Green

Greyed Green

Marine Navy

Warm Grey/Pewter

Lights: for blouses, lingerie, evening wear, warm-weather attire

Oyster White

Warm Beige

Light Gold/Buff

Light Peach/Apricot

Light Periwinkle Blue

Basic and Bright/Accent Colours: for blouses, sweaters, sportswear, dresses (can also be worn in trousers, jackets, and skirts)

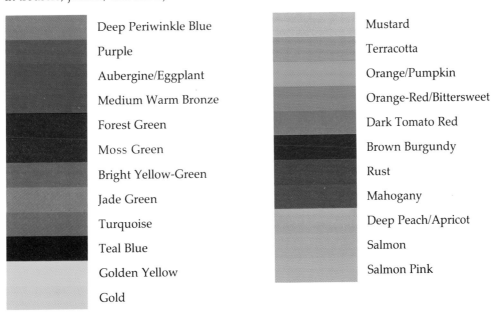

Deep Periwinkle Blue

Purple

Aubergine/Eggplant

Medium Warm Bronze

Forest Green

Moss Green

Bright Yellow-Green

Jade Green

Turquoise

Teal Blue

Golden Yellow

Gold

Mustard

Terracotta

Orange/Pumpkin

Orange-Red/Bittersweet

Dark Tomato Red

Brown Burgundy

Rust

Mahogany

Deep Peach/Apricot

Salmon

Salmon Pink

*Khaki/tan, marine navy, warm grey/pewter, light gold/buff, light peach/apricot, light periwinkle blue, purple, aubergine/eggplant, and salmon pink are new additions to the Autumn palette.*

## SPRING WARDROBE COLOURS

Spring women look best in warm, clear colours, ranging from pastel to medium bright. They wear crisp contrast well. Springs avoid dark, harsh colours, as well as blue-based pinks, reds, and greys.

Neutrals: for coats, suits, jackets, trousers, basic dresses

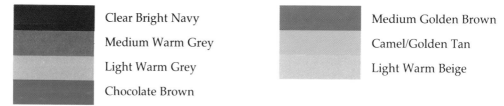

Clear Bright Navy

Medium Warm Grey

Light Warm Grey

Chocolate Brown

Medium Golden Brown

Camel/Golden Tan

Light Warm Beige

Lights: for blouses, lingerie, evening wear, warm-weather attire

Ivory

Buff

Light Peach/Apricot

Warm Pastel Pink

Light Blue/Periwinkle

Basic and Bright/Accent Colours: for blouses, sweaters, sportswear, dresses (can also be worn in trousers, jackets, and skirts)

Light Clear Navy

Light True Blue

Medium Blue

Periwinkle Blue

Dark Periwinkle Blue

Medium Violet

Pastel Yellow-Green

Bright Yellow-Green

Light True Green

Yellow-Green

Coral Pink

Clear Bright Warm Pink

Peach/Apricot

Clear Salmon

Bright Coral

Light Orange

Orange-Red

Clear Bright Red

Light Warm Aqua

Clear Bright Aqua

Light Teal Blue

Emerald Turquoise

Light Clear Gold

Bright Golden Yellow

*Clear bright navy, medium warm grey, chocolate brown, buff, light blue/periwinkle, and light teal blue are new additions to the Spring palette.*

## THE COMPLETE LOOK

NO MAKE-UP

*Look at the difference in Autumn Jennifer with and without make-up! Imagine Jennifer applying for an important job with no make-up on. But note, too, the difference when Jennifer applies only lipstick, blusher and mascara, in the minimal picture. Even though her hair is done and she's donned her earrings, her look doesn't compare to the polished image she creates by adding foundation, powder, eye shadow, liner, and brow definer. Add a scarf and necklace, too, and Jennifer has really completed her look.*

MINIMAL MAKE-UP

COMPLETE LOOK

# WINTER

NO MAKE-UP

Diane is a Winter, with light, neutral beige skin, grey-green eyes, and dark brown hair. Even though she is a beautiful girl, Diane's skin looks dull in the pumpkin-coloured blouse and orange make-up tones. In addition, Diane has applied her blusher too low, too far forward, and too heavily — a common make-up mistake. See how Diane radiates in her cool-tone royal blue blouse, hot pink lipstick, pink blusher, and silver, lavender and purple eye shadows. Her blusher lightly dusts the apple of her cheek, blending towards the upper half of her ear.

WRONG

RIGHT

## WINTER MAKE-UP PALETTE

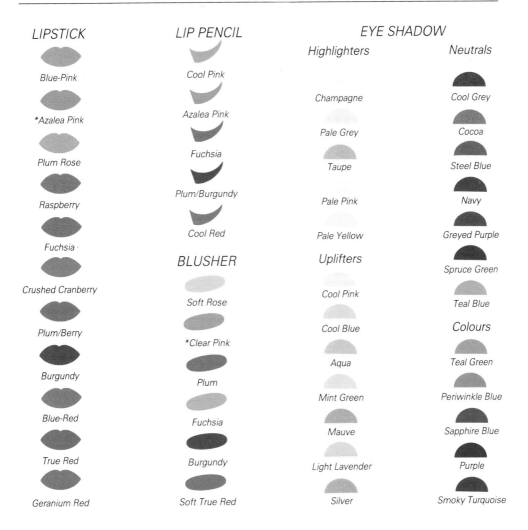

| LIPSTICK | LIP PENCIL | EYE SHADOW | |
|---|---|---|---|
| | | *Highlighters* | *Neutrals* |
| Blue-Pink | Cool Pink | | Cool Grey |
| *Azalea Pink | Azalea Pink | Champagne | Cocoa |
| Plum Rose | Fuchsia | Pale Grey | Steel Blue |
| Raspberry | Plum/Burgundy | Taupe | Navy |
| Fuchsia | Cool Red | Pale Pink | Greyed Purple |
| Crushed Cranberry | | Pale Yellow | Spruce Green |
| Plum/Berry | **BLUSHER** | *Uplifters* | Teal Blue |
| Burgundy | Soft Rose | Cool Pink | *Colours* |
| Blue-Red | *Clear Pink | Cool Blue | Teal Green |
| True Red | Plum | Aqua | Periwinkle Blue |
| Geranium Red | Fuchsia | Mint Green | Sapphire Blue |
| | Burgundy | Mauve | Purple |
| | Soft True Red | Light Lavender | Smoky Turquoise |
| | | Silver | |

**Foundations:** Sand, Cool Beige, Neutral Beige, Rose Beige, Deep Rose Beige, Rose Brown
**Basic Mascara:** Black, Black-Brown, Navy, Spruce Green
**Eyeliner:** Black, Charcoal Grey, Navy, Spruce Green, Teal Blue, Steel Blue, Deep Purple, Periwinkle Blue

*Best test colours.

## SUMMER

NO MAKE-UP

Summer Nancy has pink-beige skin, grey-blue eyes, and soft salt-and-peppery hair. See how she glows in her correct colours and make-up. Her pink blouse enhances her beauty, as does her lightly-frosted rose lipstick, rose blusher, and pink, grey, and steel blue eyeshadows. In the apricot blouse and make-up, Nancy looks sallow. Note especially the difference in eye make-up. In the 'wrong' picture, Nancy has applied dark teal eyeshadow to her lids and yellow highlighter on her brow area – exactly the wrong application technique for her eyes. Beause Nancy's lids don't show and she has a large brow area, her eyes are better complemented by applying a light shade to the lid, and a medium shade to her orbital bone, as in the 'right' picture.

WRONG

RIGHT

## SUMMER MAKE-UP PALETTE

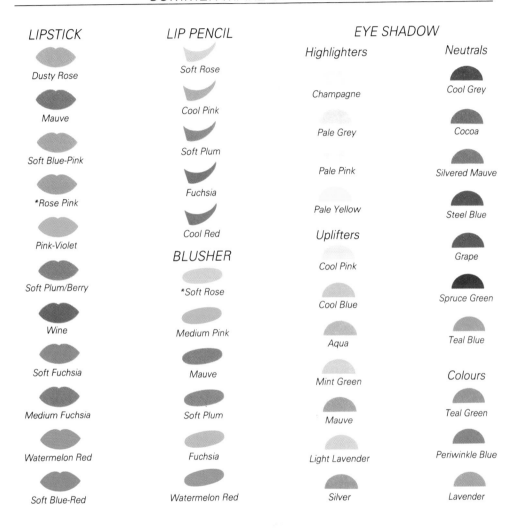

### LIPSTICK

Dusty Rose

Mauve

Soft Blue-Pink

*Rose Pink

Pink-Violet

Soft Plum/Berry

Wine

Soft Fuchsia

Medium Fuchsia

Watermelon Red

Soft Blue-Red

### LIP PENCIL

Soft Rose

Cool Pink

Soft Plum

Fuchsia

Cool Red

### BLUSHER

*Soft Rose

Medium Pink

Mauve

Soft Plum

Fuchsia

Watermelon Red

### EYE SHADOW

Highlighters

Champagne

Pale Grey

Pale Pink

Pale Yellow

Uplifters

Cool Pink

Cool Blue

Aqua

Mint Green

Mauve

Light Lavender

Silver

Neutrals

Cool Grey

Cocoa

Silvered Mauve

Steel Blue

Grape

Spruce Green

Teal Blue

Colours

Teal Green

Periwinkle Blue

Lavender

**Foundations:** Pale Pink Beige, Cool Beige, Pink Beige, Neutral Beige, Deep Rose Beige, Rose Brown

**Basic Mascara:** Brown-Black, Brown, Navy, Spruce Green

**Eyeliner:** Charcoal, Medium Grey, Taupe Brown, Spruce Green, Teal Blue, Navy, Slate Blue, Amethyst, Periwinkle Blue

*Best test colours.

## AUTUMN

NO MAKE-UP

Sharon has typical Autumn colouring: ivory skin, red hair and yellow-green eyes. She looks lovely in her forest green and orange-red clothing combination, with orange lipstick, peach blusher, and gold, peach, and brown tones on her eyes. See how her eyes sparkle. Even though fashionably dressed in black and burgundy, Sharon looks harsh when she wears these cool colours and burgundy make-up tones. Further, Sharon has made the mistake of lining her lips with a burgundy lip pencil that shows, making her lips look unnatural and severe. See how much softer she looks in her correct colours and more natural application of make-up.

WRONG

RIGHT

## AUTUMN MAKE-UP PALETTE

### LIPSTICK

Mocha

Tawny Salmon

Tawny Peach

Honey Brown

*Cinnamon

*Terracotta/Russet

Orange/Pumpkin

Mahogany

Bittersweet/Orangy Coral

Brick Red

Orange-Red

### LIP PENCIL

Mocha

Tawny Peach

Burnt Orange/Cinnamon

Orange-Red

### BLUSHER

Mocha

Salmon

*Tawny Peach

Apricot

Chestnut

Terracotta

Brick Red

### EYE SHADOW

#### Highlighters

Champagne

Beige

Warm Pink

Pale Peach

Pale Golden Yellow

#### Uplifters

Peach

Aqua

Light Warm Green

Light Violet

Gold

#### Neutrals

Coffee Brown

Golden Brown

Bronze

Olive Green

Sage Green

Putty/Warm Grey

Teal Blue

#### Colours

Teal Green

Warm Green

Smoky Turquoise

Copper

Periwinkle Blue

Violet

**Foundations:** Bisque, Ivory, Natural Beige, Peach Beige, Golden Beige, Peach Bronze, Golden Brown

**Basic Mascara:** Black, Black-Brown, Navy, Olive Green

**Eyeliner:** Brown, Olive Green, Forest Green, Teal Blue, Marine Navy, Teal Green, Violet, Turquoise

*Best test colours.

## SPRING

NO MAKE-UP

*Jill is a Spring with a delicate ivory skin tone, teal blue eyes and flaxen blonde hair. Her fair colouring is overpowered by the cool, dark red in her dress and lipstick, and the heavy, solid line of black eyeliner. In her orange-red suit, with soft poppy red lipstick and blusher, a subtle, smudgy eyeliner of medium brown, and pale eye shadow shades of champagne, peach, and brown, Jill looks young, fresh, and beautiful.*

WRONG

RIGHT

## SPRING MAKE-UP PALETTE

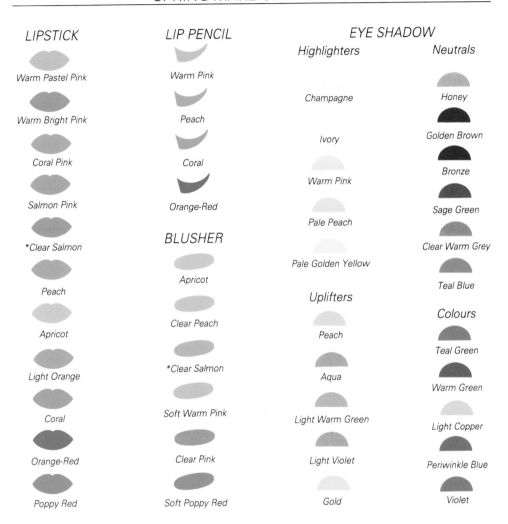

**LIPSTICK**

Warm Pastel Pink

Warm Bright Pink

Coral Pink

Salmon Pink

*Clear Salmon

Peach

Apricot

Light Orange

Coral

Orange-Red

Poppy Red

**LIP PENCIL**

Warm Pink

Peach

Coral

Orange-Red

**BLUSHER**

Apricot

Clear Peach

*Clear Salmon

Soft Warm Pink

Clear Pink

Soft Poppy Red

**EYE SHADOW**

Highlighters

Champagne

Ivory

Warm Pink

Pale Peach

Pale Golden Yellow

Uplifters

Peach

Aqua

Light Warm Green

Light Violet

Gold

Neutrals

Honey

Golden Brown

Bronze

Sage Green

Clear Warm Grey

Teal Blue

Colours

Teal Green

Warm Green

Light Copper

Periwinkle Blue

Violet

**Foundations:** Porcelain, Ivory, Peach, Peach Beige, Golden Beige, Golden Bronze
**Basic Mascara:** Brown-Black, Brown, Navy, Olive Green
**Eyeliner:** Brown, Olive Green, Sage Green, Teal Blue, Teal Green, Turquoise, Violet, Slate Blue, Periwinkle Blue

*Best test colours.

# THE
# COLOUR TEST

DETERMINING your colours is easiest with cosmetics! Trying on blusher and lipstick colours will quickly show you whether you are a Winter, Summer, Autumn, or Spring.

I've divided the Colour Test into two steps. In Step 1, you'll read the descriptions of each seasonal type and select the one or two that best describe you. In Step 2, you'll try on specific make-up colours and compare them. For this you'll need to go to a department store or a chemist that carries cosmetics tester units so you can have access to many colours.

## STEP 1: SELECTING
## THE DESCRIPTION THAT FITS YOU

As you read these descriptions, recall in your mind several outfits – past or present – that you felt terrific wearing. Did they bring you compliments? Now select the season that best describes you.

# WINTER

## Clothing

The Winter woman looks best in clear, pure cool colours, ranging from bright to dark pinks, blues, greens, purples, blue-reds, and true reds – the jewel tones. She wears dark, blue-based colours such as navy blue well, and she sparkles in black and white. A Winter doesn't look wonderful in earth tones or any muted colours. She needs brightness and clarity. Even her light colours must be clear and icy, almost like wearing white. She does not enjoy wearing pastels because they don't 'do anything' for her. The Winter woman loves to wear red.

## Make-up

Winter's best face colours are pink or burgundy blushers and medium to bright pink or fuchsia lipstick as well as true red or

### THE WINTER WOMAN

The most common Winter types have the following hair, eye colour, and skin tone combinations. Pick out the combination that best describes you, starting with your hair colour.

| Hair | Eyes | Skin |
|------|------|------|
| Black<br>Dark brown<br>Light blonde (rare) | Blue with white flecks | White<br>Rose beige |
| Black<br>Medium to dark brown | Dark brown | Olive<br>Neutral beige<br>Brown<br>Black |
| Brown | Hazel (brown/green) | Olive<br>Neutral beige |
| Brown | Green with white flecks | Neutral beige<br>Neutral beige |
| Salt and pepper<br>Silver grey<br>Pure white | Any of the above | Any of the above |

burgundy shades. Because she looks best in clear colours she often prefers a slightly frosted lip colour. The Winter woman will look drab in brown, rust, or cinnamon lipstick, and orange or peach shades will make her look sallow (yellow). If she wears a lipstick that is too pale she will look washed out. She needs colour!

## Colouring

Winter usually has intense colouring: medium to dark hair and deep eye colour. Only rarely – very rarely – is she a natural blonde as an adult. Her skin is either very white, dark (black, brown, light brown), olive, grey beige, or neutral beige. A few Winters have rosy cheeks, but most have no visible pink in their skin tone.

**Winter Women:** Elizabeth Taylor, Joan Collins, Jean Muir, Marie Helvin, Moira Stuart, Valerie Singleton.

# SUMMER

## Clothing

The Summer woman has softer colouring than Winter – lighter hair and eye colour – and therefore wears less intense colours. She is flattered by pastel to medium-bright blues, pinks, soft fuchsias, blue-greens, lavenders, mauves and aquas as well as shades of water-melon and blue-reds – all *cool* colours. She wears muted colours such as powder blue or cadet blue well. Any dark colour must be greyed down or softened a bit. She is overwhelmed by extremely bright, clear colours. Like Winter, she avoids warm, golden colours, as these will make her face look tired or drawn.

## Make-up

Summer's best blusher is soft rose or plum, and she glows in lipstick shades of rose pink, light to medium pink or fuchsia, and soft berry colours. Red lipstick is too bright for Summer unless it is a soft watermelon shade. Any orange or peach shades of lipstick or blusher will look 'brassy', and rust, cinnamon, or brownish shades will look dull.

## Colouring

The Summer is often blonde as a child, but as she matures her hair darkens to a 'dirty' blonde or an ashen brunette. A few Summers remain platinum blonde. Although never a redhead, some brunette Summers will have purplish red highlights in their hair. Summer's eyes are most often a cool blue or a grey blue, while a few Summers have green eyes, often mixed with brown. A brown-eyed Summer is a rarity indeed, except on a black or Asian woman. (Brown-eyed blondes are usually Autumns.) Summer women often have pinkish skin or a little pinkness in their cheeks. Some, however, have pale beige, very light olive, or translucent 'white' skin. Black Summers have light skin (but not golden), and Asian Summers have pale neutral beige skin.

**Summer Women:** Grace Kelly, Charlotte Rampling, Linda Evans, H.M. The Queen, the Queen Mother.

### THE SUMMER WOMAN

The most common combinations of hair, eye colour, and skin tone for Summer women are these. Pick out the combination that best describes you, starting with your hair colour.

| Hair | Eyes | Skin |
|---|---|---|
| Light to medium brown | Blue with white flecks Hazel (blue/brown) Hazel (green/brown) | White with pale pink cheeks Pinky beige Beige with pink cheeks |
| Dark blonde (ash) Platinum blonde | Blue Grey-blue Green with white flecks | Light olive Neutral beige Pinky beige |
| Dark brown | Blue with white flecks | Pale with pink cheeks Slightly ruddy |
| Soft salt and pepper Pearl grey Pearl white | Any of the above | Any of the above |
| Black Charcoal brown | Brown | Light black Light beige (Asian) |

# AUTUMN

## Clothing

The Autumn woman loves to wear rich, *warm* colours such as teal blue, bittersweet red, forest green, jade, deep salmon and peach, and coffee brown as well as earthy, muted tones of olive, rust, gold, terra-cotta, mustard, and khaki. She looks great in monochromatic outfits of beige and oyster or beige and brown, with lots of gold, brass, or copper jewellery to add warmth and richness. She usually wears muted colours better than clear colours. Even her bright colours are more flattering if they are slightly toned down. Autumns come in two varieties: light-haired ones who tend to prefer soft, earthy, neutral colours, and dark-eyed, dark-haired brunettes, and redheads who love their red, forest, and brighter colours. All Autumns avoid fuchsia, blue-reds, grey, and most pinks because they clash with their golden colouring. Most pale colours, especially blues and pinks, make them look washed out. Autumn women need rich colours!

## Make-up

The Autumn woman looks terrific in all the cinnamon, peach, russet, and terracotta shades of blusher and lipstick. Lighter Autumns love mocha and tawny peach lipsticks, while darker Autumns look better in more intense shades of terracotta or brick red. A pink or fuchsia lipstick will look harsh, even garish, on an Autumn's face.

## Colouring

The Autumn woman has hair with red or gold highlights. It may be dark blonde, resembling the 'dirty' blonde of Summer (but with more golden tones), light golden brown, chestnut, coppery brown, auburn, strawberry, or red. Some Autumns have dark brown or even black-brown hair. These Autumns can tell by the lipstick test that they are indeed an Autumn rather than a Winter! Autumn's eyes are usually brown or green. Autumn blue eyes may have golden or brown flecks in the iris, may look like steel blue from a distance, or may be teal blue or even a bright turquoise. Her skin is ivory, peach, golden beige, or brown, and may look yellow. Like Winter, she rarely has cheek colour, and needs blusher to 'come alive'. Some Autumns have ruddy skin with bright red cheeks. Autumns are never olive.

**Autumn Women:** the Duchess of York, Cilla Black, Sophia Loren, Vanessa Redgrave, Meryl Streep.

## THE AUTUMN WOMAN

These are the common combinations for Autumn hair, eye colour, and skin tone. Pick out the combination that best describes you.

| Hair | Eyes | Skin |
|---|---|---|
| Brown<br>Ivory<br>Charcoal brown<br>Chestnut<br>Coppery brown<br><br>Red<br>Charcoal black | Hazel | Dark brown<br><br><br>Yellow beige<br>Swarthy, golden beige<br>Golden brown |
| Dark golden blonde<br>Light golden brown | Dark brown | Ivory<br>Peach<br>Light beige |
| Brown<br>Auburn | Light golden brown | Ivory<br>Peach |
| Red<br>Strawberry<br>Dark blonde<br>Light auburn | Green with yellow brown flecks<br>Pale, clear green | Ivory<br>Ruddy peach<br>Golden beige |
| Chestnut<br>Golden brown<br>Red brown<br>Red | Blue with yellow or brown flecks<br>Steel blue<br>Teal<br>Turquoise | Ivory<br>Light beige |

# SPRING

## Clothing

The Spring woman shines in clear, warm colours such as light coral, peach, warm pinks, turquoise, salmon, yellow-greens, golden yellow, and orange-red. Blonde and redheaded Springs also wear camel, golden brown, peach, and apricot well. Brunette Springs especially love light royal blue, clear red, bright navy, bright golden yellow, periwinkle blue, and medium violet. Blonde Springs, unlike blonde Summers, cannot wear any muted or dark colours. Dusty mauve will look drab, and dark plum will look harsh and heavy. Brunette Springs look similar to Winters but they are not flattered by blue-based fuchsias or dark blue-reds or burgundy. Redheaded Springs can wear a few Autumn colours, but look better in the lighter, clearer colours of Spring, which give a lift to their faces.

## Make-up

Spring glows in clear salmon or warm pink blusher, and her favourite lipsticks are clear shades of salmon, coral pink, coral, or peach. Some Springs look better in pink than peach, but the pink must be a yellow-pink rather than a blue-based one. Brunette or redheaded Springs often look wonderful in clear, orange-red lipstick.

## THE SPRING WOMAN

These are the common combinations for Spring hair, eye colour, and skin tone. Pick out the combination that best describes you.

| Hair | Eyes | Skin |
|------|------|------|
| Flaxen blonde<br>Golden blonde<br>Dark blonde with<br>golden highlights | Blue with yellow<br>   flecks<br>Green with yellow<br>   flecks | Ivory<br>Peach<br>Golden beige |
| Strawberry<br>Red | Green<br>Blue | Ivory<br>Peach |
| Light brown<br>Dark blonde | Light golden<br>   brown<br>Amber | Ivory<br>Peach<br>Golden beige |
| Golden brown<br>Reddish brown<br>Neutral brown | Green<br>Blue | Ivory<br>Peach beige |
| Reddish brown<br>Neutral brown | Brown | Ivory (Asian)<br>Golden brown |

## Colouring

Springs usually have golden blonde, strawberry, light red, or golden brown hair. Some Springs have natural, flaxen blonde hair with a bright, clear look to it. A few Springs have medium to dark brown hair with or without red highlights. The majority of Springs have blue or green eyes with yellow flecks, though some have light brown or amber-coloured eyes. Spring's skin tone is ivory, peach, golden beige, or brown. A few Springs are ruddy, with pink cheeks. Black Springs are light and golden with a clear, bright look, and Asian Springs have very light, ivory skin.

**Spring Women:** Anneka Rice, the Princess of Wales, Julie Andrews, Marilyn Monroe, Paula Yates.

Now that you've chosen one or two seasons that best fit you, it's time to see yourself in make-up colours. Don't worry if you are confused by the descriptions you've just read; the make-up will tell. Seeing is believing.

## *STEP 2: COMPARING MAKE-UP COLOURS*

Unless you have bags full of cosmetics in a variety of colours, you'll need to go to a shop for this test. Wear a white blouse, as it will not clash with any make-up colours you try on. If you wear a fuchsia top and try on a cinnamon lipstick shade, it will clash with the blouse and be hard to judge.

Don't wear any foundation. The one you have at home may be wrong and could be covering up your natural skin tone. You'll determine your proper foundation after you know your season.

I'm going to describe four sets of lipstick and blusher colours, one set for each season. You can of course try on all four sets, but that's usually not necessary. Having read the descriptions, you should be able to narrow yourself to two seasons, at most three. After you've determined your season, you'll have the pleasure of investigating all the other make-up colours that will flatter you.

When you go to the shop, start with a brand that carries lots of colours. You still may need to use testers from several brands to put together your test colours. I have placed an asterisk (*) next to the best test colours on each make-up palette chart (pages 31, 33, 35, and 37) to further help you find appropriate lipstick and blusher colours.

- For *Winter*, look for a clear pink blusher (or burgundy, if you have very dark skin). Find a lipstick that is a fairly bright pink (or deep pink if your skin is dark). It doesn't have to be screaming, but it shouldn't be too pale. A slightly frosted colour is fine.

- For *Summer*, find a soft rose blusher. Then, look for a soft rose pink lipstick.

- For *Autumn*, look for a tawny peach blusher. Now find a terracotta or cinnamon lipstick shade.

- For *Spring*, find a clear salmon blusher. For lipstick, look for a soft, clear salmon. (Avoid brownish tones.)

As you try on each set, take the time to apply the lipstick carefully. Use a lip pencil if possible (see Chapter 12). You want to give each set of colours a fair look. It's hard to evaluate the attractiveness of a colour if it's improperly applied. Crooked lips, or lips with no corners, won't be appealing and will inadvertently influence your opinion of the colour.

After you try on the first set, take a good look at yourself in the mirror. It's great if you have a friend to come with you for an objective opinion. Or ask the sales assistant for her opinion.

Now remove the first set completely. Ask the sales assistant for some make-up remover. Powder your cheeks and lips with translucent powder if there is any greasy residue from the remover. Try on the next set. Which is better? If necessary, try on the third and fourth, giving each a proper application and a good look in the mirror.

Which set looks best? When I am testing clients in the stores, I can see a woman's eyes light up when we put on her 'right' colours. Sometimes I will put on the wrong colours first, just so she can see the exciting difference in the right ones. She knows that's it!

If you are still having trouble, here are a few of the most common problems:

**Blonde, blue eyes, between Summer and Spring.** Try Summer's soft fuchsia lipstick versus Spring's coral pink.

**Brunette, blue or green eyes, between Winter and Spring.** Try on Winter's true red or blue-red lipstick versus Spring's orange-red.

**Brunette, brown eyes, between Winter and Autumn.** Try Winter's true red versus Autumn's orange or brick red.

**Redhead, green or blue eyes, between Autumn and Spring.** Try Autumn's brownish shade versus Spring's delicate peach.

**Brunette, blue eyes, between Summer and Winter.** Summer or Winter both wear the same family of colours, but the intensity is different. Try Summer's soft fuchsia versus Winter's bright fuchsia.

**Blonde, green eyes, between Summer and Autumn.** Try Summer's soft pink versus Autumn's tawny peach.

If you still can't decide, you may want to go to a professional colour-and-image consultant. (See the back of the book for information.)

Once you have the general set of colours that is most flattering, you know your season. Then you can refine the look and hunt for the perfect colour and intensity for your lipstick and blusher. And you can add foundation and eye make-up for a complete look and an absolutely wonderful you.

Isn't it nice to know that with your season settled you now have the power to make perfect choices? No more wasting money on the wrong make-up. You can be wary of promotional or fashion colours – unless they are for you, of course!

Now you know your season, but don't move too fast. Before you buy any make-up, you'll want an organised plan. Cosmetics have become costly, and you want each colour you purchase to be truly useful. In the next chapter you'll learn a simple way to have a perfect selection of colours on hand so you'll look wonderful every day.

# WINTER MAKE-UP WARDROBE

### PINK

*Casual: pink lips and cheeks; eyeliner, grey; eye shadows, champagne, pink, teal.*

The Winter woman needs a lot of contrast in her clothing and make-up. She should mix her light and dark colours to balance her own natural colouring. Avoid wearing those pale ice colours alone; always accent with a bright or neutral colour.

Doreen has typical Winter colouring: light olive skin, dark brown eyes, and black-brown hair. She looks wonderful in all the cool, vivid colours of the Winter palette.

### TRUE RED

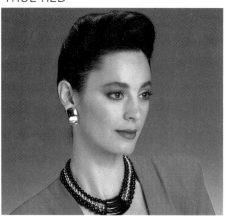

*Sophisticated: true red lips and soft red cheeks; charcoal grey eyeliner; silver and grey eye shadows.*

### BURGUNDY

*Evening: burgundy lips and cheeks; smudged black eyeliner; silver, grey, and sapphire blue eye shadows.*

### FUCHSIA (Facing page)

*Business: fuchsia lips and cheeks; eyeliner, forest green and charcoal grey; eye shadows, pink, purple, and spruce green.*

# SUMMER MAKE-UP WARDROBE

### WATERMELON RED

Casual: watermelon red lips and cheeks; slate blue eyeliner; champagne and cool blue eye shadows.

The Summer woman looks most elegant when she blends her colours softly. She doesn't want a lot of contrast because her own colouring is not very deep and is delicately balanced.

Summer Barbara has rosy beige skin, ash blonde hair and cool blue eyes. Barbara's soft colouring is enhanced by the pinks, blues and blue-greens of her Summer palette.

### BLUE-PINK

Sophisticated: blue-pink lips and rose pink blusher; charcoal eyeliner; pink, cool grey, and teal green eye shadows.

### DUSTY ROSE

Evening: dusty rose lips and rose pink blusher; charcoal eyeliner; pink, silver, and lavender eye shadows.

### SOFT FUCHSIA (Facing page)

Business: Soft fuchsia lips and cheeks; taupe brown eyeliner; mauve, cocoa, and grape eye shadows.

# AUTUMN MAKE-UP WARDROBE

### HONEY BROWN

The Autumn woman should aim for a look which blends her exciting russet tones in different ways. And if her fiery reds are too overwhelming, the salmons, jades, beiges and periwinkles in her palette provide a welcome change.

Megan's golden colouring is typical of Autumn. Her peach skin tone, dark golden brown eyes and honey hair are complemented by the rich, warm tones of Autumn's palette.

*Business: honey brown lips; chestnut cheeks; brown eyeliner; champagne, bronze, and a hint of teal blue eye shadows.*

### BRICK RED

*Sophisticated: brick red lips and cheeks; brown eyeliner; beige, putty, and coffee brown eye shadows.*

### CINNAMON

*Evening: cinnamon lips and apricot cheeks; brown eyeliner and brown kohl pencil lining inner rim of lower lid; peach, gold, and copper eye shadows.*

### ORANGE-RED (Facing page)

*Casual: orange-red lips and terracotta cheeks; brown eyeliner; golden yellow and brown eye shadows.*

# SPRING MAKE-UP WARDROBE

## CLEAR SALMON

The Spring woman's bright look is often complemented by wearing her colours in contrast – such as emerald, turquoise, coral pink and ivory. She never wants a dusty look which would make her eyes lose their sparkle.

Rebecca's creamy peach skin tone, blue eyes, and golden brown hair are true Spring qualities. Rebecca radiates in her Spring palette of warm, clear colours.

*Casual: clear salmon lips and cheeks; soft brown eyeliner; brown and peach eye shadows.*

## WARM BRIGHT PINK

*Sophisticated: warm pink lips and cheeks; brown and teal blue eyeliners; warm pink, honey, and teal blue eye shadows.*

## PEACH

*Evening: peach lips and cheeks; brown eyeliner; ivory, light violet, and bronze eye shadows.*

## ORANGE-RED (Facing page)

*Business: orange-red lips; poppy red cheeks; ivory, golden brown, and teal eye shadows.*

# CHAPTER 4

# Shopping for Your
# MAKE-UP
# 'WARDROBE'

NOW FOR the fun part – buying your make-up colours! Now that you know your season, it will be easier than ever to shop for make-up. The miracle of Colour Me Beautiful is that, because your wardrobe colours all come from one harmonious palette, you can own one blusher, one to three lipsticks, and one basic set of eye shadows and they will blend with everything you wear. Even though you have the variety of thirty-six wardrobe colours, plus many of their derivatives, their common warm or cool undertones will be complemented by the similar undertone of your season's make-up palette. Basics are a great way to start, and you'll always look terrific.

Once you get used to wearing your colours and receiving compliments, you may want to acquire some additional make-up colours from your season's palette to match the spectrum of colours in your wardrobe more precisely. It will give you that extra touch of elegance to wear a subtle red-tone blusher with a red outfit instead of your basic everyday blusher colour. Besides, we all get tired of the same thing every day, and, if you're like me, you'll want some variety.

We'll start by looking at the range of colours in your wardrobe and I'll show you which make-up colours are your most versatile basics. Then, I've included a Make-up Wardrobe Chart to give you some ideas for attractive combinations of wardrobe and make-up colours.

I've included an extra, blank chart for each season in the back of the book so you can write in specific names and brands when you shop. You may already own some make-up colours that are just right. If so, write them in. Then you can see what new colours you want to add to your collection. If you feel intimidated by adding extra colours, then stick to the basics. You'll still look great.

When selecting eye shadows, you need to take both your eye colour and clothing into account. Eye shadow colours will be discussed more fully in Chapter 11, with specific suggestions on how to flatter your eye colour. If, later, you see that one of the combinations on the chart is unflattering to your eye colour, just cross it off.

Now find the section for your season in the pages that follow. Read the explanation of your season's wardrobe colours and note the exciting ideas for make-up colours. Won't it be fun to have a 'wardrobe' of perfect make-up colours, too?

# WINTER

### Lipstick

Look again at the colour bar on page 25. The Winter wardrobe has a 'blue' end to its spectrum with blue-red, burgundy, fuchsia, and the pinks, as well as a 'warmer' end with true red and yellow. For basics, you'll need three colours: pink, true red, and fuchsia lipsticks – they will blend with all the colours in your wardrobe.

To have a perfect lipstick 'wardrobe', you can indulge in a range of pink and raspberry shades, plus a fuchsia, two or three reds, and a plum, berry, or burgundy shade. Wear a bluish red lipstick with blue-red clothing. Burgundy clothing is complemented by either burgundy, plum, or raspberry lipstick. Wear fuchsia with fuchsia (most of your other pink lipsticks will not be blue enough), and pink with pink. True red clothing needs true red lip colour, and yellow looks best with a geranium red or a pink that is not too blue.

All the other colours in your wardrobe – the neutrals, the blues, and the greens – can be worn with any of the lipstick colours from your palette, whichever are your favourites. If you love pink lips, you can wear pink with green, blue, white, or grey; or, if you are the Snow White type who radiates in red lipstick, you can wear bright red lips with all these wardrobe colours. Black clothing should be worn with a strong colour, either red or hot pink or fuchsia, because it is so strong a colour itself.

## Blusher

For perfect harmony, your blusher colour should match the tone of your lipstick – pink, red, plum, burgundy, or fuchsia – or you can buy one clear pink blusher (not too blue) which can blend with pink, red, or fuchsia lip colour. If your skin is dark, you might try a burgundy shade for your basic.

## Eye Shadow

A basic set of eye shadows would consist of a champagne highlighter, a cool grey contour shade, and either a purple, navy, spruce green, or teal blue shadow, whichever is best for your eye colour (see Chapter 11). Your dream eye shadow wardrobe could include the array of colours shown on your make-up palette (see page 31). Your eye shadows can pick up the colours from your clothing, as long as the colour looks good with your eye colour and is well blended to look subtle. With blue clothing, you can use navy or steel blue shadow; with green clothing, a mint or spruce green; with turquoise, a teal blue or smoky turquoise shadow; with purples and pinks, a purple shadow. You will always use these eye shadows sparingly, mixing and blending them with neutral colours.

---

### WINTER BASIC MAKE-UP CHART

| Lip Colour | Blusher | Eye Shadows |
|---|---|---|
| Pink (or Burgundy for dark skins)<br>True Red<br>Fuchsia | Clear Pink (or Burgundy) | Highlighter: Champagne<br>Neutral: Cool Grey<br>Colour: Purple or Navy or Spruce Green or Teal Blue |

---

### WINTER MAKE-UP WARDROBE CHART

| Clothing Colour | Lipstick | Blusher | Eye Shadows | |
|---|---|---|---|---|
| | | | Highlighter | Contour Colours |
| All Pinks<br>Magenta<br>Royal Purple<br>Icy Violet | Pink | Clear Pink | Pale Pink | Grey;<br>Purple |

## WINTER MAKE-UP WARDROBE CHART (CONTINUED)

| Clothing Colour | Lipstick | Blusher | Eye Shadows | |
| --- | --- | --- | --- | --- |
| | | | Highlighter | Contour Colours |
| True Red<br>Blue-Red | True Red<br>Blue-Red | Soft True Red | Champagne | Grey; Navy or<br>Steel Blue or<br>Sapphire Blue or<br>Spruce Green |
| Fuchsia | Fuchsia | Fuchsia | Pale Pink | Grey; Purple |
| Bright Burgundy<br>Vivid Cranberry | Plum or<br>Burgundy or<br>Raspberry | Plum or<br>Burgundy | Pale Pink | Grey; Purple<br>or Mauve or Steel<br>Blue or Navy |
| Lemon Yellow<br>Icy Yellow | Geranium Red<br>Azalea Pink | Soft True Red<br>Clear Pink | Champagne<br>Pale Yellow | Cocoa;<br>Aqua or Teal Blue<br>or Teal Green or<br>Smoky Turquoise<br>or Navy |
| Bright Periwinkle<br>Blue<br>Royal Blue<br>True Blue<br>Icy Blue | Any | Coordinate<br>with lips | Pale Grey<br>Cool Blue | Grey;<br>Sapphire Blue or<br>Navy or Steel Blue<br>or Purple |
| Hot Turquoise<br>Chinese Blue<br>Clear Teal<br>Bright Emerald<br>   Turquoise<br>Icy Aqua | Pink<br>Fuchsia | Pink<br>Fuchsia | Pale Grey<br>Aqua | Grey;<br>Smoky Turquoise<br>or Teal Blue or<br>Teal Green or<br>Greyed Purple |
| Light True Green<br>True Green<br>Emerald Green<br>Pine Green<br>Icy Green | Any | Coordinate<br>with lips | Champagne<br>Mint | Cocoa;<br>Spruce Green<br>or Purple<br>or Navy |
| Black<br>White<br>Navy<br>All Greys | Any | Coordinate<br>with lips | Icy Grey | Grey;<br>Any |
| Black-Brown<br>Taupe | Any | Coordinate<br>with lips | Champagne<br>Taupe | Cocoa;<br>Any |

# SUMMER

### Lipstick

Study the colour bar on page 26. The Summer wardrobe has a 'blue' end to its spectrum with blue-red, burgundy, soft fuchsia, mauve, plum, and the pinks, and a 'warmer' end with watermelon red and light lemon yellow. For a basic lipstick collection, you will need three shades: rose pink, soft fuchsia, and watermelon red.

For a complete lipstick wardrobe, you can collect a range of pink and rose shades, as well as a soft fuchsia, a mauve, a plum or wine, and a couple of soft reds. With blue-red clothing wear a bluish red lipstick. With burgundy, choose a wine or plum lipstick. Wear fuchsia with fuchsia; with mauve and plum clothing wear mauve or plum; with pinks wear pink or rose. Watermelon red clothing needs to be paired with a watermelon shade of red lipstick. With yellow, choose watermelon red or a pink lip colour that is not too blue. All the other colours in your wardrobe – the neutrals, blues, and greens – can be worn with any of the lip colours on your make-up palette, whichever most flatters you.

### Blusher

Your blusher colour ideally should harmonise with your lipstick, so, for a perfect blusher collection, you would buy a soft rose or a medium pink, a soft fuchsia, a soft plum or mauve, and a watermelon red. For a basic blusher, however, a soft rose (not too blue), will go with pink, red, or fuchsia lip colour.

### Eye Shadow

A basic set of eye shadows, to go with everything, would consist of a champagne highlighter, a cool grey neutral, and either steel blue, greyed grape, spruce green, or teal blue eye shadow, whichever best complements your eye colour (see Chapter 11). Your extended shadow wardrobe can include practically all the colours shown on your make-up palette (see page 33). Your eye shadows can pick up colours from your clothing, as long as the shadow colour looks good with your eye colour and is well blended to look subtle. With blue clothing you can wear steel blue shadow; with green clothing, mint or spruce green; with aqua and turquoise an aqua or soft teal; and with pink, plum, or mauve, use a grape shadow. You will always use these eye shadows sparingly, mixing and blending them with neutral shadow colours.

## SUMMER BASIC MAKE-UP CHART

**Lip Colour**

Rose Pink
Soft Fuchsia
Watermelon Red

**Blusher**

Soft Rose

**Eye Shadows**

Highlighter: Champagne
Neutral: Cool Grey
Colour: Steel Blue or
      Grape or Spruce
      Green or Teal
      Blue

## SUMMER MAKE-UP WARDROBE CHART

| | | | Eye Shadows | |
| Clothing Colour | Lipstick | Blusher | Highlighter | Contour Colours |
| --- | --- | --- | --- | --- |
| All Pinks<br>All Roses<br>Lavender<br>Orchid<br>Medium Violet | Rose<br>Pink | Soft Rose<br>Medium Pink | Pale Pink | Cool Grey;<br>Grape or<br>Lavender or<br>Silvered Mauve |
| Watermelon Red<br>Blue-Red | Watermelon Red<br>Soft Blue-Red | Watermelon Red | Champagne | Cool Grey;<br>Steel Blue or<br>Spruce Green<br>or Teal Blue |
| Soft Fuchsia | Soft Fuchsia | Soft Fuchsia | Pale Pink | Cool Grey;<br>Silvered Mauve or<br>Grape or Spruce<br>Green or Steel<br>Blue |
| Plum<br>All Mauves<br>Raspberry<br>Burgundy/<br>Maroon | Soft Plum/Berry<br>Mauve<br>Wine | Soft Plum | Pale Pink | Cool Grey;<br>Grape or<br>Spruce Green or<br>Steel Blue or<br>Silvered Mauve |
| Light Lemon<br>Yellow | Watermelon Red<br>Pink | Watermelon Red<br>Medium Pink | Pale Yellow<br>Champagne | Cocoa; Aqua or<br>Teal Blue or Teal<br>Green or Mint |

## SUMMER MAKE-UP WARDROBE CHART (CONTINUED)

| Clothing Colour | Lipstick | Blusher | Eye Shadows | |
|---|---|---|---|---|
| | | | Highlighter | Contour Colours |
| Powder Blue<br>Sky Blue<br>Cadet Blue<br>Medium Blue<br>Periwinkle Blue | Any | Coordinate<br>with lips | Champagne<br>Pale Grey | Cool Grey;<br>Cool Blue or<br>Steel Blue or<br>Grape |
| All Aquas<br>Soft Teal | Any | Coordinate<br>with lips | Champagne<br>Aqua | Cocoa or<br>Cool Grey;<br>Aqua or Teal Blue<br>or Grape |
| All Blue Green<br>Spruce Green | Any | Coordinate<br>with lips | Champagne<br>Mint | Cocoa; Mint or<br>Spruce Green or<br>Teal Green or Grape |
| Greyed Navy<br>Greyed Blue<br>Light Blue-Grey<br>Charcoal<br>Blue-Grey | Any | Coordinate<br>with lips | Champagne<br>Pale Grey | Cool Grey; Steel<br>Blue or Grape or<br>Silvered Mauve |
| Soft White<br>Rose Beige<br>Rose Brown<br>Cocoa | Any | Coordinate<br>with lips | Champagne | Cocoa;<br>Any |

# AUTUMN

### Lipstick

Look again at the colour bar on page 27. The Autumn wardrobe ranges from the warm orangish side – with orange-red, orange, pumpkin, terracotta, and golden yellow – to the 'cooler' end – with salmon pink and brown burgundy. For basic set of lipsticks, you'll need two colours: a cinnamon or terracotta and a salmon. A great cinnamon will blend with everything in your closet except the salmons and salmon pinks.

To have an ideal lipstick wardrobe, you can indulge in a range of cinnamon, terracotta, mocha, and peachy colours, a tawny salmon, one or two reds (say, a brick and an orange-red), plus an orange and a mahogany. Your red clothing will look best with a red lipstick; with orange, pumpkin, and yellow clothing, choose an orange shade; with terracotta and rust, wear a terracotta lip colour. Peach will look most harmonious with a tawny peach lipstick. On the other hand, the pinkish colours in your wardrobe, especially your salmon pink, need to be paired with a salmon lip tone.

All the other colours in your wardrobe – the neutrals, greens, and blues – can be worn with any of the lipstick colours from your palette, whichever are your favourites. Whether you prefer a brownish tone, a peach, or a bright orange-red, you can successfully pair any with your olive or forest green, brown or tan, periwinkle blue, or teal blue clothing. Your warm pewter, because it is greyish, looks best with either a red or mahogany lipstick, rather than a brown one.

## Blusher

Your blusher colours ideally should match your lipstick – peach, chestnut, terracotta, brick red or salmon. For a basic, buy a tawny peach, which will harmonise reasonably well with all your colours. If your skin is very fair, try a lighter apricot shade.

## Eye Shadow

A basic set of eye shadows, to blend with everything, would consist of a champagne highlighter, a bronze contour shadow, and either a teal blue, smoky turquoise, olive green, warm green, or copper eye shadow, whichever is best for your eye colour (see Chapter 11). Your dream eye shadow wardrobe could contain all the colours on your Autumn make-up palette (see page 35). Your eye shadows can pick up colours from your clothing, as long as the shadow is attractive with your eye colour as well. With blue clothing, you can wear periwinkle; with teal and turquoise, teal shadow; with pumpkin, orange, or brown, choose peach and copper shadow; with greens, wear warm green shadow. Of course you'll want to mix these eye shadows with some of your neutral shades, so they don't look too bright.

---

### AUTUMN BASIC MAKE-UP CHART

| Lip Colour | Blusher | Eye Shadows |
|---|---|---|
| Terracotta or Cinnamon | Tawny Peach | Highlighter: Champagne |
| | | Neutral: Bronze |
| Tawny Salmon | | Colour: Teal Blue or Smoky Turquoise or Olive Green or Warm Green or Copper |

## AUTUMN MAKE-UP WARDROBE CHART

| Clothing Colour | Lipstick | Blusher | Eye Shadows | |
|---|---|---|---|---|
| | | | Highlighter | Contour Colours |
| Orange-Red/ Bittersweet Dark Tomato Red | Orange-Red Brick Red | Brick Red | Champagne | Coffee Brown; Smoky Turquoise or Warm Green or Copper |
| Brown Burgundy Mahogany | Mahogany Mocha | Mocha | Warm Pink | Coffee Brown; Bronze or Copper |
| All Peaches/ Apricots | Tawny Peach | Tawny Peach Apricot | Pale Peach | Golden Brown; Teal or Copper |
| Orange/Pumpkin Terracotta Rust | Orange-Pumpkin Terracotta | Terracotta Chestnut | Champagne Pale Peach | Golden Brown; Copper or Warm Green or Teal Blue or Teal Green |
| Light Gold/Buff Gold Golden Yellow Mustard | Cinnamon Terracotta Tawny Peach Orange-Red | Apricot Tawny Peach | Champagne Pale Golden Yellow | Golden Brown; Teal Blue or Green or Aqua or Bronze |
| Purple Aubergine/ Eggplant | Orange-Red Orangy Coral Salmon | Brick Red Salmon | Champagne | Bronze; Violet or Warm Green |
| Salmon Pink Salmon | Tawny Salmon | Salmon | Warm Pink | Putty; Smoky Turquoise or Warm Green |
| Teal Blue Turquoise Jade Green | Any | Coordinate with lips | Champagne Aqua | Bronze; Teal Blue or Teal Green or Smoky Turquoise |
| All Periwinkle Blues | Any | Coordinate with lips | Champagne Beige | Putty; Periwinkle Blue or Violet or Copper |

## AUTUMN MAKE-UP WARDROBE CHART (CONTINUED)

| Clothing Colour | Lipstick | Blusher | Eye Shadows | |
| | | | Highlighter | Contour Colours |
| --- | --- | --- | --- | --- |
| Bright Yellow-Green<br>Forest Green<br>Olive Green<br>Moss Green<br>Greyed Green | Any | Coordinate with lips | Champagne<br>Beige | Bronze;<br>Olive Green or<br>Sage or<br>Warm Green or<br>Copper |
| Oyster White<br>Warm Beige<br>Khaki/Tan<br>Camel<br>Coffee Brown<br>Dark Brown/<br>Charcoal<br>Medium Warm<br>Bronze<br>Warm Grey/<br>Pewter | Mocha<br>Honey Brown<br>Any | Mocha<br>Chestnut<br>Coordinate with lips | Champagne | Coffee Brown;<br>Any |
| Marine Navy | Any | Coordinate with lips | Champagne | Putty;<br>Any |

# SPRING

## Lipstick

Take another look at the Spring colour bar on page 28. Notice that the Spring woman's wardrobe colours range from orange-red, orange, peach, and yellow on the 'warm' end, to pinks and violet on the 'cooler' end. For basic lipsticks, choose a clear salmon and a poppy red. Because salmon is a cross between orange and pink, it will blend with your peaches, pinks, and even violet, as well as the neutrals, blues, and greens. You'll need poppy to wear with your reds.

To have a complete lipstick wardrobe, you could treat yourself to a range of corals and salmons, a peach, one or two warm pinks, a poppy red, and perhaps a light orange. Orange-red looks best with an orange-red lipstick; orange and peach clothes with peach lipstick;

yellow clothing with either peach or coral; and pink and violet clothes with a pink lip colour.

The other colours in your wardrobe – the neutrals, greens, and blues – can be paired with any lip colour from your palette. Choose your favourite. Warm pink, peach, coral, and even your orange-red lipstick will harmonise equally well with your ivory, navy, yellow or kelly green, periwinkle or aqua clothing.

## Blusher

An ideal blusher wardrobe would contain clear salmon, apricot or peach, a warm pink, and a soft poppy red to match your various lip colours. But for a basic, buy a clear salmon, as it will blend reasonably well with everything.

## Eye Shadow

A basic set of eye shadows, to go with everything, would be a champagne highlighter, a golden brown contour shade, and either a teal blue, periwinkle blue, peach, or warm green eye shadow, whichever best complements your eye colour (see Chapter 11). Your dream shadow wardrobe can include all the colours on your make-up palette (see page 37). Your eye shadows can pick up colours from your clothing as long as the shadow is flattering to your eye colour. With blue clothing you can wear periwinkle blue shadow; with aqua and emerald turquoise, a teal or aqua; with peach, orange, and orange-red, a peach shadow; with green clothes, choose a warm green shadow. You will want to use these eye shadows sparingly, and mix and blend them with neutral shadow colours.

---

### SPRING BASIC MAKE-UP CHART

| Lip Colour | Blusher | Eye Shadows |
|---|---|---|
| Clear Salmon<br>Poppy Red | Clear Salmon | Highlighter: Champagne<br>Neutral: Golden Brown<br>Colour: Teal Blue or Periwinkle<br>Blue or Peach or Warm<br>Green |

---

## *SPRING MAKE-UP WARDROBE CHART*

| Clothing Colour | Lipstick | Blusher | Eye Shadows | |
| --- | --- | --- | --- | --- |
| | | | Highlighter | Contour Colours |
| Warm Pastel Pink Coral Pink Clear Bright Warm Pink Medium Violet | Warm Pink Coral Pink | Warm Pink Clear Pink | Warm Pink | Warm Grey; Violet |
| Clear Salmon | Clear Salmon Salmon Pink | Clear Salmon | Warm Pink | Honey; Teal Blue or Warm Green |
| Bright Coral | Coral | Clear Salmon Soft Poppy Red | Pale Peach | Golden Brown; Light Copper |
| All Peaches/ Apricots Light Orange | Peach Apricot Light Orange | Clear Peach Apricot | Pale Peach | Golden Brown; Teal Blue or Warm Green or Sage or Light Copper |
| Orange-Red Clear Bright Red | Orange-Red Poppy Red | Soft Poppy Red | Pale Peach | Golden Brown; Bronze or Light Copper or Teal Blue |
| Buff Light Clear Gold Bright Golden Yellow | Peach Clear Salmon Coral | Clear Peach Clear Salmon Poppy Red | Ivory Pale Golden Yellow | Golden Brown; Bronze or Aqua or Teal Green or Periwinkle Blue |
| All Yellow-Greens Light True Green Kelly Green | Any | Coordinate with lips | Champagne Pale Golden Yellow | Golden Brown; Warm Green or Sage Green or Bronze |
| All Periwinkle Blues Light True Blue Medium Blue | Any | Coordinate with lips | Champagne | Honey; Periwinkle Blue or Violet |
| All Aquas Emerald Turquoise Light Teal Blue | Any | Coordinate with lips | Aqua | Honey; Teal Blue or Teal Green or Aqua |

## SPRING MAKE-UP WARDROBE CHART (CONTINUED)

| Clothing Colour | Lipstick | Blusher | Eye Shadows Highlighter | Contour Colours |
|---|---|---|---|---|
| Ivory<br>Light Warm<br>  Beige<br>Camel/Tan<br>Medium Golden<br>  Brown<br>Chocolate Brown | Any | Coordinate<br>with lips | Ivory<br>Champagne | Honey;<br>Any |
| Light Warm<br>  Grey<br>Medium Warm<br>  Grey<br>Light Clear Navy<br>Clear Bright<br>  Navy | Any | Coordinate<br>with lips | Champagne | Warm Grey;<br>Any |

## SHOPPING FOR MAKE-UP

With your Make-up Wardrobe Chart and your season's printed make-up palette, you are now ready to go shopping!

But even armed with charts and colours, it can still be somewhat overwhelming to look at a tester unit brimming with colourful products. It's hard to know where to begin. Take heart, there is a foolproof *system* to make it easier. Whether you are shopping for foundation or lipstick, the same steps apply.

Let's take lipstick. First, separate the lipsticks into warm and cool colours (you'll learn how in later chapters) and pull out the ones that might be for you. Line them up on the counter in order of shades, from light to dark. Start in the middle and try on the medium shade. If it's too dark, put it back in the tester and forget the darker colours. Now try on the next lightest colour, then the next lightest, and so on, until you've found the right shade for you. Often the colour in the tube, pan, or bottle doesn't look the same on your skin, so trying on the middle shade gives you a starting point. This system also keeps the colours organised, so you don't forget which ones you've already tried on. You'll quickly know whether or not this cosmetic line carries your perfect colour. If it does, you've found your colour quickly. If not, you needn't agonise. Simply move on to another counter.

This shopping system works especially well for products that are removable from the tester unit. Blushers and eye shadows are usually glued to the unit, so you can't line them up, but you can still use the same principle of starting with the middle shade and then moving lighter or darker.

Often you will not have to do this testing all by yourself. Most sales assistants with the major cosmetic lines are familiar with colour analysis and are trained beauty advisers, so you will find them quite knowledgeable. Together you can use the 'line 'em up, try on the middle' method for finding your perfect shades.

Be sure to check the shade in natural light. Most stores use fluorescent lighting, so you may need to borrow a hand mirror and go to the shop entrance or window to evaluate the colour. As you try out new products, ask yourself if the colour is right (too blue? too yellow?), if the value is flattering (too dark? too light?), and if the colour is clear or muted enough for you. You'll soon pinpoint exactly what's right for you!

The beauty adviser can assist you with make-up application. Most of us still love to have personal attention and guidance. If you are not experienced or comfortable with make-up, ask her for help. Tell her *frankly* the look you want. If you feel she is wearing too much make-up for your comfort level, explain that you would like a more natural look. Don't feel intimidated. I assure you the beauty adviser is eager to help you, and a good adviser will always work at your comfort level, not hers.

Shopping for make-up will be more fun than ever now that you know what you're looking for. You won't make costly mistakes, and you can be sure you have invested in good choices that will work for you. Now it's time to bring your make-up home, unwrap all the pretty boxes, and organise your new goodies so they're ready to use at a moment's notice.

## ORGANISING YOUR MAKE-UP

You'll get the most out of your exciting new colours if you buy an attractive plastic organiser and keep your make-up, like your wardrobe, convenient and organised. Place lipsticks in one compartment, blushers in another. Often these organisers have holes for mascara wands and lip and eye pencils. By keeping your make-up orderly and at your fingertips, you'll save time getting dressed in the morning. When I timed myself at putting on my make-up, I noticed that I lost minutes if I had to hunt for a certain eye pencil or lipstick. I can put on all my make-up – foundation, concealer, powder, blusher, eyeliner, eye shadow, mascara, and lipstick – in six minutes if I have everything assembled where I need it. An organised 'wardrobe' starts the day off smoothly.

Now it's time to acquire the tools you will need to apply your make-up so it looks naturally beautiful – just like you!

# BEAUTY TOOLS

**H**AVE you ever tried to paint a thin line with a thick brush or with a brush that had hairs sticking out and refused to make a point? I have. My first entrepreneurial venture was a biscuit ornament business. I fashioned little 'people' out of salt dough, stuck a Christmas hook in their heads, baked them, and painted them: I painted intricate patchwork designs on their dresses and, of course, each had to have a smile, rosy cheeks, and long eyelashes. After painting a number of lopsided smiles and lumpy lashes, I learned the job was impossible without a very thin, pointed sable brush. With the right brush, the job was easy.

Before you begin the make-up lesson in Part II, you need the right tools. With good tools, you can control the amount of colour you want, blend colours, and correct minor mistakes. Even the finest cosmetics will look streaky applied with poor applicators.

Many women don't buy special brushes because they think they aren't necessary. The tiny applicators inside shadow and blush containers are convenient for touch-ups, but they will not produce as natural and blended a look as fullsize quality brushes you purchase separately. After only one practice session, you will use good brushes for ever. They will last for years, and you'll never regret the investment.

Do try to buy only natural hair brushes. Natural hair is gentle to your face, lasts longer, maintains its shape, and allows you to control the application. The weight of natural hair also gives a brush the best balance. Pony, goat, sable, camel, and squirrel hairs are commonly used in brushes. Don't panic if your brushes shed a few hairs when new. If they continue to shed after a week or so, however, return them.

Professional-quality brushes and applicators are easy to find in most department stores. Buy a set, if you can, or purchase individual brushes as you can afford them. Packaged as a set, brushes are usually less expensive than buying each separately.

Brush sets often come in a roll-type pouch. This is great for travel, but not convenient for daily use. I like to store my brushes upright in a plastic or ceramic cup, something pretty. Make sure your container is not too light, however, or it might fall over from the weight of the brushes. If you travel often, I strongly recommend that you treat yourself to a separate travel-size brush set and keep it permanently packed in your suitcase. One summer holiday when I forgot to pack my brushes I couldn't believe how much harder it was to apply my make-up. It took me twice as long, and the final result was less than satisfactory.

The following brushes would make an ideal, complete set. They are described in the order you would use them. You'll learn more about how to use these brushes in the chapters that follow. If you can't buy a full set just yet, start with a blusher brush, powder brush, eye fluff brush, and eye sponge. Add, too, a lip brush, to outline your lips evenly, unless you plan to use a lip pencil.

### Under-eye Brush

An under-eye brush is like a thin, flat paintbrush, about ¼ inch (5mm) wide, and is used to apply concealer or coverstick to dark under-eye circles or lines around the mouth. Also, it's wonderful for highlighting cheek bones. I like to have two of these brushes so I can use the second one to 'smudge' eyeliner and soften its effect. Ideally, this brush should be made of natural, resilient sable.

### Powder Brush

This, the largest brush in your collection, is used to fluff on loose or pressed powder. It should be slightly rounded in shape and very full. Select soft hair such as pony, squirrel, goat, or a combination.

### Blusher Brush

The blusher brush is one of your most important tools. Smaller than the powder brush but similar in shape and composition, it's used to apply and blend your blusher. This brush ideally should contain some sable, as sable has enough body to help 'move' the blusher where you want it on your cheek. Correct placement of your blusher is vital, so please don't skimp on the quality of your blusher brush.

### Contour Brush

The contour brush looks like a blusher brush that has been cut straight across the top. The flat, stubby shape is great for removing excess blusher, blending the edges of your blusher or eye shadow, or for contouring.

### Fan Brush

You'll have fun with this thin, soft, fan-shaped brush. Because of the softness of its hair (usually goat), it provides a light application of any powder product. It's ideal for gently removing excess loose powder, for applying iridescent powder at night, or for applying a touch of bright blusher when you want the application to be very light. Turned sideways, it can be used to 'hollow' your cheekbones with a contour powder.

### Eyeliner Brush

This thin, fine-tipped brush is used wet to apply cake eyeliner or to turn your eye shadow into an eyeliner. Select a brush made of sable so it is resilient, not too soft, and holds its point. If you have blemishes, you can buy a second brush and use it to dot coverstick on the problem spots for extra coverage after foundation has been applied.

### Eye Shadow Sponge

An eye shadow sponge will apply shadow more heavily than the brush, so it is best for applying light to medium colours or any shadows where you want more coverage. A clean sponge is also great for blending stubborn edges, 'erasing' mistakes, or – turned sideways – for 'smudging' eyeliner to soften its effect. Eye sponges are not expensive, so you'll want to have several. Be sure the applicator is made of cosmetic-grade sponge, which is smooth to the touch. If the sponge looks very porous or is scratchy, don't buy it.

## Eye Shadow (Fluff) Brush

The fluff brush is a miniature version of your blusher brush – the same shape and hair. It will give you a light application of eye shadow, and is especially good for dark colours where you don't want too much. You'll also use it for blending.

## Eye Contour (Angle) Brush

This brush is my favourite because it gives you so much control in the placement of your shadow. Your 'angle' brush looks like an under-eye brush that has been sliced diagonally. The shape of the brush is great for fanning shadow along the orbital bone. Here, sable is best, to give the brush substance.

## Brow and Lash Brush/Comb

One side of this handy tool looks like a thin, stiff toothbrush, the other like a tiny comb. Use the brush to groom and shape your eyebrows, and use the comb to gently separate your lashes after applying mascara.

## Lipstick Brush

You'll become an expert painter when you use this flat, narrow brush to line your lips and apply lipstick. No lopsided lips for you! Sable is essential for your lipstick brush because it is stiff enough to spread the colour and hold its shape for maximum control. I especially like the compact, retractable type because you can carry it in your handbag for touch-ups.

Be sure to wash your brushes periodically in mild detergent, then remove excess water with a towel. Don't soak them or the wooden handles will crack. Smooth and shape the hairs on the brushes and lay your damp brushes flat on a towel to dry. They'll dry more quickly if you let the hair extend over the edge of the dressing table so air can circulate. Be careful not to dry your brushes in an upright position, as water may seep into the wooden handles. If you prefer, you can use alcohol, which won't harm natural hair, to clean and sterilise your brushes. Wash at least one eye sponge every day so it will be clean and dry for the next day's use.

In addition to brushes, there are several other tools you'll need. Most are available at any good chemist.

## Cosmetic Sponge

Cosmetic sponges are used to apply and blend foundation. If you are not sure of the composition, make sure the pores of the sponge are almost invisible and that the sponge feels smooth against your skin. The sponges usually come in triangle or diamond shapes, so the pointed corners can get into the nooks and crannies around your nose and eyes. You may also use your sponge for blending down blusher or shadow, if you find you've applied too much. It's a good idea to have several on hand and wash them frequently so you always have a clean, dry one for blending.

## Cottonwool Balls or Pads

These are primarily used for applying skin-care products such as liquid cleansers, tonics, and eye make-up remover, but they can also be used for blending and softening eye shadows and blush. If you have sensitive skin, make sure you buy real cottonwool rather than synthetic balls and pads. Synthetic fibres can be abrasive and are also less absorbent than cottonwool.

## Cottonwool Buds

You can use buds to 'smudge' and blend eyeliners and shadows, or to remove mascara mistakes.

## Tissues

Tissues are handy for wiping up spills or cleaning brushes, but use them sparingly on your skin. Paper is made of wood fibre, and the slightly rough texture can irritate sensitive skin.

### Tweezers

Tweezers are for plucking stray hairs from your eyebrows. You have a wide selection of styles from which to choose, but my favourite type resembles a pair of scissors.

### Eyelash Curler

This tool requires great care and a steady hand. (You don't want to break off or pull out your lashes.) It works on a clamp-pressure principle, putting a crimp in your lashes so they curl upwards. Rinse the rubber pad after every use and have an extra one available if you use the curler often. Curl your lashes first, then apply mascara.

### Sharpener

If you use lip or eye pencils, a sharpener is an absolute must. Many pencil products come with a sharpener, but if not, you can use the type sold with school supplies. If you find your soft lip pencils or smudgeliners breaking in the sharpener, try popping them into the freezer for a few minutes before sharpening.

### Mirrors and Lights

If you don't have good lighting in your make-up area, you may want to purchase a mirror with lights. Many have adjustable light settings that duplicate the lights in an office, daytime, evening, or home setting. No one stays in one place all day, so set your mirror on the brightest setting so you can see what you're doing. Good lighting that doesn't cast a shadow is more important than the colour of the light (unless you are going out for dinner and want to know how you'll look in an evening setting). A magnifying mirror is handy when you are plucking your eyebrows or if you have difficulty seeing in a normal mirror.

_SHOPPING LIST_____

Here is a list of all your beauty tools. Use it as a basic shopping guide.

Under-eye Brush

Powder Brush

Blusher Brush

Lipstick Brush (two – one for handbag)

Brush Cup

Contour Brush

Fan Brush

Eyeliner Brush

Eye Shadow Sponges (two)

Eye Shadow (Fluff) Brush

Eye Contour (Angle) Brush

Brow and Lash Brush/Comb

Cosmetic Sponges (several)

Cottonwool Balls or Pads

Cottonwool Buds

Tissues

Tweezers

Eyelash Curler

Sharpener

Magnifying Mirror and Lights

Now you have everything you need to become your own make-up artist. You're almost ready to begin your adventure into the Make-up Lessons. But first, if you're going to be an artist, you need to prepare your canvas. . . .

# Part II

# THE MAKE-UP LESSON

# CHAPTER 6

# SKIN CARE

YOU'VE found your season, you know your colours, you've assembled your beauty tools – but wait! Before you put even a dab of make-up on your face, you *must* have skin that's squeaky clean and well cared for. If you skimp on skin care, nothing that comes after will look its best.

When I do makeovers on my promotional tours, I frequently find women whose skin is parched and dry, even rough. When I ask what skin care products they use, I often hear, 'Well, I wash my face with whatever soap is in the bathroom, and sometimes throw on a little moisturiser.' Such skin, abused by harsh body soap and starving for moisture, will slurp up the foundation, leaving it thick and cakey-looking. Not only will poor skin care wrinkle your skin prematurely, but you will also be depriving yourself of one of your potentially greatest assets – beautiful skin.

I can understand a woman's reluctance to move from soap and water into a modern skin-care routine. With so many new products on the market, we all have been confused about which to buy and how to use them. I assure you, however, that the benefits are well worth the effort of learning how to pamper your skin. All our grand-mothers had was soap and cold cream to combat the ageing process, but we have the benefit of recent dramatic breakthroughs in skin-care research and products. Now there are special new ingredients – especially enzymes and vitamins – that help retard wrinkling and keep our skin looking smooth and supple.

You are probably wondering if you have time for an elaborate skin-care routine. Don't panic. I promise you, it takes longer for me to describe the routine and the products than it will for you to use them.

The general principles of skin care show good common sense. First, you thoroughly clean your skin, occasionally using a scrub to remove dead skin cells. (The accumulation of those dead cells is what causes rough, scaly skin.) Then, you soften and tone your skin with a toner or astringent, which also helps your skin maintain its elasticity. Next – and this is the new part – you *nourish* the cells while they are growing so they will arrive at the surface as round and plump as possible (the only part of our bodies we like to have plump!). Then you seal in your skin's moisture with a moisturiser. And, last, you lubricate your eye area. The whole routine takes five minutes or less. Time yourself. You'll see.

Every couple of weeks or so, you may also want to bleach or remove excess facial hair, if you have any. Some women need to pluck and shape their eyebrows, or bleach or wax off a moustache. Then your skin will be smooth, free of fuzz, and ready for make-up. You'll love the results.

## DETERMINING YOUR SKIN TYPE

Before I explain your routine, let's take a minute to identify your type of skin, since this will affect your skin-care regimen. Filling in the questionnaire that follows, you'll learn whether your skin is dry, normal, oily, or a combination. Women with combination skin have normal cheeks but an oily forehead, nose, and chin (commonly called the T-zone).

In the chart on the next page, circle the answers that apply to your skin and then add up your responses in each column. The column that contain the most circles determines your basic skin type. If your circles are split fairly evenly between two columns, place yourself in the oilier category. It's better to err on the side of a regimen that is less rich, since over-rich products can cause spots. You can always switch to richer products if you need them.

You may need to reassess your skin type from time to time. Many factors – a personal crisis, stress, getting married or divorced, pregnancy, taking on a new job, taking certain medications, or simply

*The T-zone is the T-shaped area formed by the forehead, nose, and chin. These areas tend to be oilier than the cheeks.*

getting older – can affect your skin. Often a change in climate or environment will affect your skin's balance. During hot, humid weather your skin may become so oily that you'll need little or no moisturiser. During the winter, cold weather, heated houses, and dry air can parch even normal and combination skins. Be sensitive to how your skin looks and feels. Adjust your regimen to use more, or less, of any product, depending on your skin's needs. If, for example, your skin is on the borderline between normal and oily, you may want to skip your moisturiser for several days during oily bouts. Or, your skin may need products for dry skin during the wintertime, but those for normal skin during the summer months.

Don't forget that what you put into your body affects your skin. Eat plenty of fruits and vegetables – the high-water-content foods – and drink pure water to hydrate your skin from the inside. Avoid fats, caffeine, and cigarettes. Fats are indigestible, caffeine overstimulates the adrenal glands, and both can cause spots and increased oil production. Cigarettes constrict the blood vessels, limiting the oxygen supply to the skin (look at the wrinkles around the eyes of a heavy smoker). Get sleep so your skin can rest. Get aerobic exercise so your whole body gets the benefit of increased circulation.

Your skin is the largest organ in your body! It reflects the condition of your health and your spirit. Take good care of it.

## ASSESSING YOUR SKIN TYPE

| Question | Dry | Normal/ Combination | Oily |
|---|---|---|---|
| Do you break out in spots? | Rarely | Occasionally | Frequently |
| Do you have blackheads? | Few or none | Some in T-zone | Problem |
| What do your pores look like? | Nearly invisible | Visible in T-zone | Enlarged |
| After washing with soap, how does your skin look and feel in one hour, without a moisturiser? | Dry and tight | Slightly tight for the first half hour, comfortable or with some oil in T-zone by the end of an hour | Oily in half an hour; shiny nose and forehead in one hour |
| What is your colouring? | Very fair; fair | Fair to medium | Olive to dark |
| Do you have facial lines? | Some around eyes, lips, forehead | A few around eyes | None or very few |
| How do you respond to the sun? | Burn easily | Usually burn first, then tan gradually | Rarely burn, tan easily |

## STEPS TO GOOD SKIN CARE

With your skin type in mind, you're ready to choose the products that will enhance your lovely skin, and to master your skin-care programme so it will be as natural as brushing your teeth. There are five basic categories of skin-care products: *cleansers, toners, nourishers* (which include cell-renewal formulas), *moisturisers,* and *special eye-area lubricants.* As we go through the five steps of a basic skin-care regimen, we'll look at each product and the role it will play in your personal routine. You'll find specific information for your skin type in the skin-care charts on pages 91 to 93.

Shopping for skin-care products will be easy because each cosmetics company designs formulas for the different skin types. I strongly suggest that you purchase the same brand for all your skin-care needs. The products within each line are designed to work together; if you buy cleanser from one company, nourisher from another, and moisturiser from a third, you risk getting too much of one ingredient or not enough of another.

## STEP 1: CLEANSING

The cornerstone of your skin-care programme is cleansing – getting your face deepdown clean but without stripping it of its essential oils. You'll need to buy a special facial cleanser and use it twice a day, just as you brush your teeth. (You can take it into the shower, if you like. See – you don't have to change all your habits!) Cleansers come in a range of forms – liquids, gels, creams, oils, and bars (facial soaps).

Gently massage your cleanser in an upward and circular motion to thoroughly remove dirt from under the downy facial hairs and the surface of the pores. Use your fingertips, a soft flannel, or a cosmetics brush (my favourite!). Turn a boring task into a treat by giving your face a mini-massage each time you cleanse.

### Supercleansing

Your daily cleansing will leave your skin clean and soft, but occasionally you will want to supplement it with a supercleanser – a special scrub or mask designed to remove dead skin cells and to deep-clean your pores. Dead cells, if allowed to remain, can cause roughness and can also lead to whiteheads or bumpiness. If you use a cellular renewal product, which generates new cell growth quickly, your supercleansers are especially important.

Scrubs are mildly abrasive, and are primarily for removing dead skin; masks help cleanse the pores. Both invigorate and stimulate the skin. You can use either scrub or mask, or both – with scrub first followed by your mask. You will *love* the way your skin feels. As with other skin-care products, scrubs and masks come in formulas especially for your skin type, so be sure to check the labels.

**Scrubs** These often contain cleansing grains. Choose one with small, smooth grains such as ground nuts or oatmeal. Avoid those that contain nut shells or kernels, as these are rough and abrasive.

If your scrub comes in a tube, squeeze out a teaspoonful onto the palm of your hand. If your scrub comes in a jar, use a spatula or small spoon. (It's best not to put your finger in the jar, as you risk depositing bacteria.) With your fingertips, massage the scrub into your skin for several minutes in an upward, circular motion on your face and neck, avoiding your eye area. Rinse thoroughly with warm water. Mmmmm! What smooth skin you have!

**Masks** Some masks contain mud and clay-based compounds that absorb excess oils and draw out dirt and impurities. These mud masks are meant for normal and oily skin types and should not be used by women with dry skin.

Special moisturising masks, usually made with honey, cleanse and mildly stimulate the skin and also attract moisture from the air, helping to plump up the cells on the surface of your skin. Although these masks are primarily for dry skin, any skin type can benefit from a moisturising mask from time to time, especially when the weather is cold and dry, or if skin has been exposed to excessive wind or sun.

Apply your mask in a thin, even layer, avoiding your eye area. If you use a mud mask, allow it to dry and become 'stiff'. The hydrating masks do not stiffen. Follow the directions on the package, and be careful not to overdo – more time is *not* better, especially with a mud mask. Now, gently rinse off your mask with warm water and pat your face dry with a clean, soft towel.

## STEP 2: TONING

After cleansing – and supercleansing – you apply your toner. Your toner (which may be called a 'freshener' 'astringent', 'rinse', or even 'skin softener') will remove any last traces of cleanser and excess oil, temporarily tighten your skin's surface, and return your skin to its normal pH level, thus protecting it from bacteria. (Cleansing removes the protective 'acid mantle' from your skin, and it takes your body about twenty minutes to restore it by itself.) Many toners also have ingredients to soften the skin, making it ready to receive the nourishers or moisturisers to follow.

Toners are applied with a cottonwool ball or pad, again in an upward direction, from the base of your throat to your hairline. Don't rub hard; it doesn't help the toner clean any better and can harm your skin. Avoid the delicate eye area, as any toner can be drying. Use your toner twice a day, following your regular cleansing or super-cleansing with a scrub or mask. Toner leaves your face feeling ting-ling and refreshed.

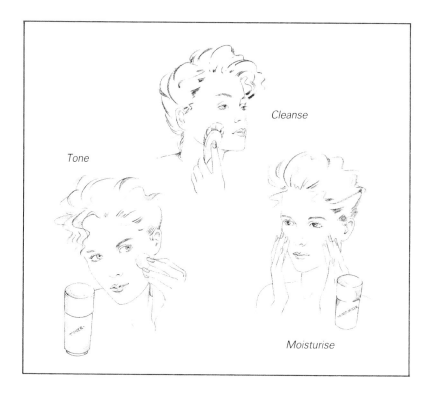

## STEP 3: NOURISHING

The next step toward beautiful skin is nourishing, an amazing new concept that has emerged from skin-care research over the past five or six years. All skin types can benefit from nourishers, which work underneath the skin's surface, feeding the internal layer of growing cells so they will mature plump and healthy. Nourishers include cell-renewal products as well as wrinkle creams and 'anti-ageing' lotions, all of which aim to combat the wrinkling process before it begins. A woman will usually begin using a nourisher in her late twenties, when her cell growth begins to slow down.

Nourishers are applied sparingly. They are usually thin, non-greasy, and meant to be followed by moisturiser. Most of the cell-renewal products come in a bottle with an eye dropper. You simply squeeze three to five drops on your fingertips and feather them on to your face. For the creams, you dab just a little on your fingertips and again feather onto your face. Allow these products to dry for a minute or two before applying moisturiser. Use nourisher twice a day, following your toner.

## *STEP 4: MOISTURISING*

Now it's time to lubricate and protect the surface of your skin. Moisturisers will not 'erase' wrinkles and cannot repair damaged or ageing skin. They do, however, contain humectants, substances that attract water from the air and hold it to the surface of the skin, which helps plump the surface cells. In addition, they contain sealers to hold in the skin's own moisture (water) and to prevent impurities from entering the pores.

A word of caution: never use petroleum jelly as a moisturiser – it suffocates the skin, causing the pores to enlarge (permanently) in the skin's desperate effort to breathe. Also avoid moisturisers with mineral oil as it too prevents the skin from breathing. Your skin needs oxygen as much as you do!

Whatever your skin type, keep in mind that your skin's moisture needs will vary. The way your skin feels in the best guide. If your skin starts to feel taut, itchy, or rough, it may be time for you to try a richer formula. On the other hand, if you are getting shiny spots on your forehead and nose, or if your skin starts to break out in spots, switch to a lighter product. Everyone needs to use moisturiser on the neck because, without oil glands, it is one of the first areas of our body to show ageing.

Apply a thin coat of moisturiser from the base of your throat to your hairline, or in drier areas only, using gentle, upward strokes. Avoid your eye area, as the humectants in the moisturisers can puff up the skin and can cause swelling around your eyes. This will actually stretch the skin and cause wrinkles. Apply just enough moisturiser to do the job. Once again, more is not better; the excess will simply pool on the surface of your skin.

## STEP 5: LUBRICATING YOUR EYE AREA

Your skin regime so far has avoided the area around your eyes. Why? Because the skin in your eye area is devoid of oil glands, is extra-thin and delicate, is prone to wrinkling, and needs special care. You need eye cream – different from your moisturiser – with special ingredients and no humectants.

Before lubricating your eye area, you need to thoroughly remove your eye make-up. It's important to remove your eye make-up every night with utmost care. Always use special eye make-up remover, rather than soap, which is too drying. Eye make-up remover comes in liquid, gel, and cream forms and in oily and non-oily formulas. I prefer the non-oily kind for regular use because it's not greasy and if you accidentally get some in your eye, it won't blur your vision. Also, it's wonderfully handy to have around for repairing eye make-up mistakes. A cotton bud dipped in eye make-up remover can erase unwanted dots of mascara or eye shadow like magic without ruining the rest of your make-up. If you are removing waterproof mascara, you'll need to purchase one of the oily formulas specifically for waterproof mascara. Any eye make-up remover should not sting. If it does, it undoubtedly contains an ingredient to which you are sensitive, so switch to another brand.

To use eye make-up remover, dab a small amount on a cottonwool ball, wipe downward on your upper lid, and then across under your lower lashes, from the outside corner in. Don't saturate the cottonwool, or you can wash make-up into your eyes.

After you've completely removed your eye make-up, you're ready to lubricate the skin around your eyes. Eye creams vary from heavy ointments to lightweight creams and gels, and are formulated for all skin types. The ointments are better for night because they are a bit sticky, while the lighter weight products can be worn even under make-up. Look for a formula containing vitamin E, an excellent natural lubricant.

To apply eye cream, use your ring finger – it's the weakest – so you won't stretch or pull your skin. Gently pat a tiny amount of cream along your orbital bone (the one that encircles your eye). Don't apply the cream too close to your lashes, as the warmth of your body can make it melt and spread into your eye. Use eye cream twice a day, following moisturiser.

If your eyes are red and puffy from allergies, too much sleep, or even from crying, you also might want to try one of the wonderful new eye gels designed specifically to combat puffiness. These gels

*The orbital bone is the bone that surrounds your eye.*

reduce the accumulation of water under and around the eyes and leave them feeling cool and refreshed. You simply pat the gel on the puffy area before you apply eye cream.

Following are skin-care regimen charts, summarising the steps for each skin type. I've included the regimens again at the back of the book on a chart you can cut out. I like to keep the regimens for all three types sellotaped to the inside of my medicine cabinet. Then, if I need to adjust my routine for any reason, I have all the steps handy for easy reference. You might also want to consider lining up your products in order in your medicine cabinet or wherever you will keep them, and numbering them with stickers or a marking pen. I found that when I first added nourisher and scrub to my regimen, I spent a fair amount of time reading labels, trying to remember what came after what. After a few days of practice, you'll know your routine by heart. And, in a few short weeks, you'll really see a difference in your beautiful skin!

## FACIAL HAIR

### Upper Lip

Some of us are 'blessed' with a fuzzy moustache on our upper lip. Take heart, however, as it's easy to bleach it so the hairs will become blonde and barely noticeable. There are several excellent products easily obtained at a chemist, designed especially for facial hair. If your moustache is thick, I recommend having it removed. The hairs will interfere with the application of your lipstick and ruin your lovely lipline. One option is to wax it off, which is temporary and must be repeated every so often. Most beauty salons offer waxing as a service, or you can buy a waxing kit at a chemist and do it yourself. If you prefer, you can have hair permanently removed by means of electrolysis at an accredited beauty salon.

## Eyebrows

You may also want to shape your eyebrows by plucking hairs that stray too far down on your orbital bone. Your eye shadow won't look as attractive if you have to apply it on top of stray hairs, plus a nice, arched brow will open and lift your eyes. Go easy here, however. Thin or thick eyebrows may or may not be the fashion, but whatever the vogue, never overpluck your brows. Plucked eyebrows often will not grow back. A natural look, neither too thin nor too thick, is timeless and always flattering.

Because your eyebrows frame your eyes, it's important that the length of your brow be in proportion to your eye. The illustration shows you how to determine the proper length.

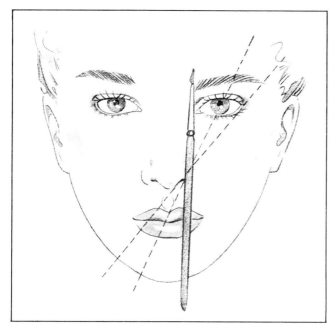

*Pluck stray hairs from the ends of your brows, as well as under the arch.*

First place a pencil or long-handled brush from the outer edge of your nose to your tear duct. Then place it from your nose to the crease at the outer edge of your eye. Pluck any stray hairs that extend beyond these boundaries. Then pluck the stray hairs underneath your brows. Create a gentle arch, following the shape of your eyes, with the peak at the outside of your pupil. Place your pencil or brush handle from your nose to your pupil to find where the peak of your brow should be.

## *SKIN-CARE REGIMEN FOR DRY SKIN*

### Step 1: Cleansing

Choose a cream, liquid, or oily cleanser. These can be rinsed off with warm water or, if your skin is extremely dry, just wiped off with a soft, clean cloth. If you prefer a soap, choose one that is superfatted and made with emollients and moisturisers specifically for dry skin.

*Supercleansing*. Alternate using a gentle scrub or a honey mask formulated for dry skin once a week after using your regular cleanser. It's OK to use both, on occasion, with mask following scrub, as long as your skin is not extremely sensitive. Caution: Mud masks are not appropriate for dry skin.

### Step 2: Toning

Follow cleansing/supercleansing with toning. You need a toner with no alcohol, since alcohol is too harsh for your skin. Look for a toner that includes witch hazel, the non-drying ingredient most often substituted for alcohol that also helps tighten the surface of the skin. If your skin is *very* dry, you may want to use toner only once a day.

### Step 3: Nourishing

Apply a few drops of a cell-renewal product or one of the 'anti-ageing' creams specifically labelled 'nourisher', not moisturiser.

### Step 4: Moisturising

Chose a rich moisturiser for daytime and night cream for night. During the winter, you may even want to use your night cream in the daytime if your skin feels rough or chapped. Don't forget to moisturise your neck.

### Step 5: Lubricating your eye area

Use an eye cream morning and night.

| A.M. | P.M. |
| --- | --- |
| Cleanser | Eye make-up remover |
| Toner | Cleanser |
| Nourisher | Toner |
| Rich moisturiser | Nourisher |
| Eye cream | Night cream |
|  | Eye cream |

## *SKIN-CARE REGIMEN FOR NORMAL OR COMBINATION SKIN*

### Step 1: Cleansing

Try a liquid cleanser or facial bar soap, whichever you prefer. Liquid cleansers for normal skin must be rinsed off, as they usually contain a mild facial detergent, an ingredient not found in products for dry skin.

*Supercleansing*. Use a scrub or mask (or both) formulated for normal or combination skin once a week after using your regular cleanser.

### Step 2: Toning

Try a non-alcohol toner in the wintertime or in drier climates when your skin might tend to become a bit dry or sensitive. In warmer, more humid climates, you can use an astringent with a small amount of alcohol.

### Step 3: Nourishing

Apply a few drops of cell-renewal product or other skin-nourishing product of your choice. You may want to apply this product only at night, especially if you are oily in the T-zone.

### Step 4: Moisturising

Choose a lightweight moisturiser for the summer and a slightly richer one for the winter. In the wintertime you may also want to use a night cream. If you have combination skin, use moisturiser only on the cheeks and neck, leaving the oily T-zone alone. After five minutes, if your skin feels at all sticky, pat a cottonwool ball slightly dampened with toner over your face to remove excess moisturiser that wasn't absorbed.

### Step 5: Lubricating your eye area

Use an eye cream morning and night.

| A.M. | P.M. |
|---|---|
| Cleanser or facial soap bar | Eye make-up remover |
| Toner/Astringent | Cleanser or facial soap bar |
| (Nourisher) | Toner/Astringent |
| Moisturiser | (Nourisher) |
| Eye cream | Moisturiser or Night cream |
| | Eye cream |

## *SKIN-CARE REGIMEN FOR OILY SKIN*

### Step 1: Cleansing

Most women with oily skin prefer the feel of a facial soap. Try an oatmeal soap, for its mild abrasiveness will remove dead cells that tend to cling to oily skin. You might also want to help remove excess oil by filling your basin with hot water and rinsing your face with twenty splashes to steam open your pores. Be careful not to wash your face too often in an effort to rid it of oil. Twice a day is enough. If stripped of all its oils, your clever skin will pump overtime and you'll be oilier than ever.

*Supercleansing.* Use a scrub formulated for oily skin twice a week and a mask once a week after using your regular cleanser.

### Step 2: Toning

Select an astringent with alcohol listed as one of the first five ingredients. Look for products with boric acid, which is antibacterial and helps absorb oil.

### Step 3: Nourishing

Use a lightweight nourishing product, preferably one with little or no oil. Usually the cell-renewal liquids (the ones that come with the eyedropper) are best for oily skins. Use only at night if your skin is very oily.

### Step 4: Moisturising

You may not need moisturiser for your face – your skin's own oil is often enough – but do moisturise your neck. During the dry winter months, you may want to use a lightweight moisturiser on your cheeks. Some companies produce moisturisers specifically formulated for oily skin – effective in keeping the surface of the skin smooth without adding unwanted oil. If your skin breaks out in spots, it's best to skip all moisturiser (except on your neck). Your skin will dry out as you age so you will eventually need to use moisturiser. If moisturiser seems sticky five minutes after you have applied it, pat a cottonwool ball slightly dampened with astringent over your face to remove what wasn't absorbed.

### Step 5: Lubricating your eye area

Use an eye cream morning and night.

| A.M. | | P.M. | |
|---|---|---|---|
| Cleansing bar | Moisturiser on | Eye make-up | Moisturiser on neck |
| Astringent | neck or as | remover | or as needed |
| (Nourisher) | needed | Cleansing bar | (Astringent/Toner) |
| | (Astringent/Toner) | Astringent | Eye cream |
| | Eye cream | Nourisher | |

## . . . AND THE REST OF YOU

Don't neglect the rest of your body, either. Always keep legs and underarms free of stubbly hair. Follow every bath or shower with lotion on legs, arms, hands, and elbows, perhaps using a favourite scented lotion, to prevent itchy dryness. And, every now and then, indulge in a 'Day of Beauty'. A day of relaxation and special attention to your needs will enhance your inner beauty, as well as your skin.

By the way, your husband or your boyfriend can use the same products you do. Men's skin-care lines are packaged differently, but the products are the same. His skin needs tender loving care just as much as yours. Why not have a facial night together once a month or so – a chance to indulge, and turn off the cares of the world.

## INGREDIENTS AND SENSITIVITIES

Most of today's skin-care products are a combination of advanced scientific technology and select herbs and botanicals with a proven history of gentle soothing and healing. Many of our great-grandmothers' home remedies really did work!

Skin-care products typically contain *emollients* (mostly oils and silicones to seal in moisture and soften the skin), *humectants* (to add more moisture), *protectants* (to heal and soothe), *emulsifiers* (to make the ingredients work together), *preservatives* and *antioxidants* (so the product won't spoil), as well as the herb and plant extracts and the newer 'special' ingredients.

Unfortunately, not all skin-care products list the ingredients used. The best products should include hyaluronic acid (to add moisture), collagen amino acids (protein to nourish the growing cells), hydrolised elastin (to add moisture and enhance elasticity), retinol (vitamin A), and vitamin E (an emollient and an antioxidant, which supposedly helps prevent ageing through cellular breakdown). Products that are in amino acid form have molecules that are small enough to penetrate the surface layer of your skin and help those baby cells that are still growing. Products that say 'soluble' have heavier molecules, and work only on the surface of the skin.

Some natural ingredients that are especially beneficial are sesame, sweet almond, and wheat germ oils (emollients), lanolin (a waxy emollient and an excellent skin softener), allantoin (to protect, heal, soothe, and inhibit allergic reaction), the queen bee's 'royal jelly' (vitamin B), as well as extracts of aloe vera, apricot kernel, birch leaf, chamomile, clover blossom, coltsfoot, rosemary, and sage (to either soften, soothe, or stimulate the skin).

## A DAY OF BEAUTY

A Day of Beauty is a lovely way to make you feel as special as you are. Just follow these easy steps:

1.  Start by washing your hair, using your favourite shampoo.
2.  Then fill the bath with clean, comfortably warm water and the additives of your choice – a nice bubble bath or a scented bath oil to soften your skin.
3.  While the bath is running, towel dry your hair and apply a generous amount of deep conditioner. Don't rinse your hair yet, just cover it with a shower cap and then wrap it in a towel to let your conditioner penetrate slowly.
4.  Now slip into the bath. Soak for a full five or ten minutes, banishing all your tension and worries. Then:
•  Work a pumice stone over your feet, heels, and elbows to smooth away rough calluses.
•  Lather up a loofah sponge with your most luxurious soap and gently stroke it upwards, from your toes to your shoulders, concentrating on rough spots.
5.  Rinse yourself off, then step out of the bath and blot yourself dry with a towel.
6.  Smother yourself with a rich body lotion, maybe in your favourite fragrance, massaging it especially well into the dry areas of your body.
7.  Wrap up in your warm terry towel bathrobe.
8.  Now that your face is nicely steamed from your bath, cleanse it well, massaging it lightly with your fingertips to smooth away muscle tension. Rinse, and give your face a once over with your scrub to leave it glowing and super smooth.
9.  Now treat yourself to a mask, according to your skin type. Apply the mask in your bathroom and then, while the mask works, lie down on your bed, feet up, eyes closed, muscles relaxed, mind serene – perhaps with your favourite music in the background.
10.  Now, return to the bathroom to rinse the mask off with warm water, and rinse the conditioner out of your hair. You'll want to keep your pampered body dry, so rinse your hair in the basin – first with warm water, then cool. Towel dry your hair and comb it out gently. Give it a chance to dry free in the air, a rest from the blow dryer.
11.  Finish your 'facial' with toner, nourisher, moisturiser (if needed), and eye cream. Pat eye cream onto your lips as well for an extra soothing touch.
12.  If you can keep the world at bay a little longer, curl up with a hot cup of herb tea and a good book.

Don't panic if your skin breaks out in spots a bit after you begin a new skin-care regimen, especially if you hadn't been caring for it beforehand. Your new cleansing regimen will open your pores and pull dirt and hardened oils to the surface, possibly causing temporary blemishes. If you are still having problems after two or three weeks, you may be using a product that is too rich, or you may be allergic.

Allergies usually cause redness and irritation rather than blemishes. Before throwing out your entire regimen, first check for other culprits. Have you begun or stopped using any medication? Changed your shampoo, your mousse, or your washing detergent? Used a new nail varnish, hand cream, or perfume? Even a change in weather and the arrival of pollens or moulds can suddenly make you seem 'allergic' to a product.

Then, too, make sure that you are following directions carefully. If a cleanser says 'rinse thoroughly', not doing so could leave detergent on the skin and result in itching.

If you do have an allergic reaction to a product, you'll have to read labels and be a detective to hunt down the offending ingredient. There is no such thing as a nonallergenic product. Even hypoallergenic lines can contain ingredients that cause reactions in some people. Buying a product that says 'allergy tested' does mean, however, that the product does not contain commonly irritating ingredients.

Some ingredients that can irritate sensitive skin are sodium laurel sulphate (a detergent), fragrances, preservatives, and some oils. Almond oil, lanolin, and vitamin E, in spite of their wonderful properties as emollients, can irritate certain very sensitive skins. Mineral oil should be avoided in moisturisers, but does an excellent job in cleansers that are washed off. If you have acne-prone skin, avoid products in which oil is one of the first few ingredients, and do consult a dermatologist. Treatment for acne has improved dramatically over the last five years.

Good skin care takes only minutes a day, and it can make such a dramatic difference! Your face is the image you present to the world. It's worth a little bit of time and effort to keep your skin healthy and glowing.

# FOUNDATION

J
UST AS an artist prepares a canvas with a special, neutral wash to even out its surface colour and imperfections, your face needs foundation to smooth its texture and to even out its tone.

My first experience wearing foundation was appearing in my school play, when the director had us put on theatrical pancake make-up. It was so greasy and heavy that my face felt dirty, and after that experience I shied away from foundation for years. I couldn't believe the difference when I tried it again. Modern foundation products are sheer, light, and comfortable. You won't even *feel* a foundation if the product is right for you.

Some women avoid foundation because they think it will clog their pores. Ironically, these same women will apply blusher and eye shadows directly on their skin, a practice that is far more likely to clog pores. Foundation actually protects your skin (and your pores) from dirt and pollutants and helps reduce moisture loss from the sun and the wind.

## CHOOSING THE RIGHT COLOUR

The key to a natural look is choosing the right colour foundation, one that harmonises with your skin tone. Women often tell me that finding a foundation to match their skin is a frustrating job. How well I remember 'matching' my olive skin, only to turn orange an hour later! Don't despair. Finding the perfect colour is going to be easier now that you know your season.

I recommend shopping for foundation in a department store that supplies testers, rather than in a chemist, where all the packages are sealed. Foundation in the bottle usually looks darker than it does on skin, so you really have to try it on to judge.

To find the perfect foundation, you need to identify the range of shades apropriate to your season. If you are a Winter or a Summer, you want to find *cool* or rose-based shades. Usually colours labelled *rose*, *sand*, *mahogany* or *neutral* are cool. Autumns and Springs should look for *warm* or yellow-based shades. These often are called *porcelain*, *ivory*, *peach*, *golden*, *bronze* or *natural*. If you find colours with nondescriptive names such as Beige Delight, ask the sales assistant if she knows which colours in her line are rose-based or yellow-based.

If she doesn't know, you will have to judge by eye. Some colours will be obviously pink or peach, but other shades will appear to be more neutral. It is difficult to evaluate a colour that's standing by itself, so look at several shades together for comparison. Put blobs of three or four colours on the back of your hand. Which ones have a pink or purplish cast? These are the cool shades, best for Winters and Summers. The warm shades, for Autumns and Springs, are the ones that look slightly yellow or peachy.

Once you've identified the cool and warm shades, you can narrow them down to the colour that's right for you:

• *Winters:* a cool, neutral shade, if you are olive, Asian or black; a slightly rosy beige if you have visible pink in your skin; a pale, sand colour if you are very fair.

• *Summers:* a pinkish beige if you have visible pink in your skin; a neutral cool shade if your skin is more beige than pink.

• *Autumns:* a warm peach if you have ruddiness or lots of freckles; ivory if you are fair and slightly creamy; a warm 'natural' beige if your skin is beige; golden beige if your skin is quite golden.

• *Springs:* a warm peach or pinky peach, if your face is ruddy or you have 'high colouring'; porcelain or ivory if your complexion is creamy and light; golden beige if your skin is darker and golden.

Choose the warm or cool foundation that most closely matches your natural skin tone. As a final step, you must test a foundation on your face, preferably on the jawbone. The skin on your wrist and hand varies tremendously from the skin on your face. Don't try to match the colour to your cheeks, either, as they may be rosier than the rest of your complexion. Avoid 'adding colour' to your face with a foundation that is darker than your skin. You will have an unnatural line around your jawbone, and you will look older. Actually, a shade of foundation that is a smidge *lighter* than your skin makes you look more youthful. Give it a try, but don't go too light or your face will appear chalky.

When shopping, use the Foundation Test chart below to help you choose the perfect colour of foundation.

Once you have found your perfect foundation shade, you'll want to reevaluate it from time to time. The sun, your diet, the medications you take, tension, and your general state of health may affect your

## FOUNDATION TEST CHART

**1.** Using your season as a guide, select two or three shades of foundation that are in the right colour range for you.

**2.** Making sure your face is clean and free of make-up, apply thin stripes of each foundation along your jawline with downward strokes.

**3.** Wait a few minutes and observe each shade as it dries. If possible, check the results in natural light. The wrong shade will 'sit' on your face, leaving an obvious stripe. If the colour is right, it will blend into your skin with the *edges* almost disappearing. If none of these shades is perfect, repeat the process. You may have to go on to the next make-up counter to try another brand.

**4.** Once you find the best colour, remove the stripes and reapply it on your jawline, this time blending it in. It should be imperceptible.

**5.** When you think you have found the right foundation, apply it to your entire face right from the testers and wear it for a while. If it still looks great after an hour, you've made the right choice. If it has turned chalky, the foundation is either too light or too cool a shade for you. If it has turned orange, the foundation is either too dark or too warm a shade for you, or it contains too much oil.

skin colour and, in turn, the way your make-up looks. When tanned, apply the same warm and cool principles, but select a darker shade of foundation.

## CHOOSING THE RIGHT FORMULAS

Foundations come in three basic formulas: water-based, oil-based, and oil-free. Most of today's modern formulas are water-based liquids, creams, mousses, or cakes with a small amount of oil, designed to give a sheer to medium coverage. These foundations are suitable for most skin types and are designed to be worn over your moisturiser and other skin-care products. They are not meant to be substituted for proper skin care. A proper skin-care regimen will provide your skin with the moisture it needs so your foundation can be light and comfortable. Water-based formulas apply smoothly with a cosmetic sponge and are easy to work with.

If you have extremely dry skin, you may want to consider an oil-based foundation in which oil is one of the major ingredients. These foundations tend to have thicker coverage, which can accentuate wrinkles, but they do give extra protection to dry skin, especially in the wintertime or in cold climates.

Oily skins, especially those that break out in spots, usually need an oil-free formula. Women with slightly oily skin may want to switch to an oil-free foundation in the summertime or in any hot, humid climate. Oil-free formulas do not spread easily, but they are a blessing for those women plagued with excessive oil. Apply them with your fingertips, let dry, and then 'buff' your face with a dry cosmetic sponge. Because these formulas consist of mostly water and powder, the buffing technique works well to smooth out the application. Some brands are so thin they can be applied with a cottonwool ball before being buffed. An oil-free foundation cannot be used around the eye area as it is too drying. You will need to buy a second foundation with some oil content to apply around your eyes, or use a cover-stick there instead. In either case, choose a similar or slightly lighter colour.

To check the oil content of a formula, read the label. Ingredients are listed in order of predominance. In an oil-based formula, oil is the second or third ingredient (water is always first); in a water-based formula, oil is in the middle or near the end; an oil-free formula obviously has no oil.

You might also ask the sales assistant what kind of coverage a product offers. If you have clear, beautiful skin, you need only a light, sheer coverage. To cover average skin with a few imperfections, medium coverage is desirable. Heavy formulas are best reserved for the stage, unless you have a major problem with skin discolouration. If you have problem skin, you may be tempted to reach for more coverage, but a heavy formula will both accentuate and aggravate raised blemishes and is best avoided.

*Caution:* Never add water to your foundation to make it more sheer. Water will not only change the chemical balance of your product, but may also add irritating bacteria. If you want sheerer coverage, apply your foundation with a dampened cosmetic sponge, or choose a lighter formula.

## INGREDIENTS AND SENSITIVITIES

Foundations consist primarily of water, talc, oil, pigments, various additions to benefit the skin, preservative, and, sometimes, fragrance.

Ingredients that benefit all skin types are aloe (a skin softener), soluble collagen (to maintain suppleness of the skin's outer layer), hyaluronic acid (to add moisture), hydrolised elastin (to enhance elasticity), and PABA (sunscreen).

If you have allergies or sensitive skin, choose foundations with almond, sesame, or avocado oils. These natural oils are known for their soothing properties and low level of irritation. Even though mineral oil is a natural substance, you should avoid it unless your skin is very dry, for its heaviness can make it hard for skin to breathe. Lanolin is an excellent emollient, but in large amounts it can irritate sensitive skin. Most foundations contain very little, however, so don't scared off if it appears at the bottom of the list of ingredients.

If you are prone to acne, stay away from foundation containing oil (except perhaps as one of the last ingredients), fragrance, and detergents such as sodium laurel sulphate and laureth-4. In addition, some dermatologists feel that isopropyl myristate may exacerbate problems in acne-prone skin. This ingredient helps improve absorption of emollients, a plus for dry skin, but a potential problem for those who break out in spots from excessive oil.

## SPECIAL CONCEALING PRODUCTS

In addition to foundation, you may want to consider buying one of the special concealing products created to give additional coverage to problem areas: coverstick, colour adjuster, or eye shadow base.

*Apply coverstick, or concealer, with your under-eye brush to dark areas around eyes, nose, mouth, and chin. Pat with fingertip to blend.*

**Coverstick** is a spot concealer designed to minimise dark circles under the eyes, 'smile lines' (shadows that run from the nose to the corner of the lips), the shadow between lip and chin, or the occasional blemishes nearly all of us suffer. A coverstick comes in a lipstick-type tube, or occasionally in a wand, in light, medium, and dark. I recommend buying a colour as similar to your foundation shade as possible, or slightly lighter. A shade that is too light, applied under the eyes, will make you look like an owl.

When applying coverstick under the eyes, dot the coverstick on your under-eye brush and apply coverage just on the dark ridges where you need it. Applying concealer on the whole under-eye area will make your eyes look puffy. Blend by patting with your fingertip.

You can apply concealer *under* foundation, *on top* of foundation, or *by itself*. I prefer to apply it on top, and then pat to blend, for the most natural look. For a severe under-eye problem you may want to apply your concealer more heavily and then cover with foundation, but do pat the foundation on gently or you risk removing the coverstick. If you choose to wear coverstick alone under your eyes, be sure the colour is compatible with your foundation.

**Colour adjusters** are products designed for people with extremely ruddy (red) or sallow (yellow) skin. They are similar in texture to foundation, only thinner. They come in tubes, wands, or bottles, and are applied under foundation. Buy an aqua shade to neutralise ruddy skin; use a lavender shade to perk up sallow skin. For ruddiness, apply a thin coat with a cosmetic sponge just on the ruddy areas, usually the cheeks. For sallow skin, thinly coat your forehead, cheeks, and chin.

**Eye shadow base** is applied to the upper eye area, the lid, and the underbrow, and helps cover veins or very dark lids. In addition, it helps hold your eye shadow on all day, and prevents eye shadow from creasing. For this reason, many women like to use it on the upper eye area instead of foundation, even if they don't have a problem with veins or dark lids. It comes in a mascara-type wand, a tube, or a little pot, usually in one neutral shade. You apply it with the wand, your fingertips, or a clean eye sponge applicator, and blend with your cosmetic sponge. You do *not* apply foundation on top of eye base. Black skins do not need this product for coverage, but may want a thin eye base just to hold the shadow on better. These thinner bases usually come in taupe, silver, or gold – almost transparent shades.

If you have a serious problem with scars or pigment discolouration, there are some specialised products available. Usually they are pre-scribed by dermatologists.

## APPLYING FOUNDATION

With all the elements assembled – your foundation, concealers, cosmetic sponges, and brushes – you're all set to start working make-up magic! Don't be daunted. It takes less than a minute to apply foundation. Add another minute if you want to use coverstick and eye base. Add a third if you need colour adjuster. With practice, your whole routine, including powder, blusher, eye shadow, mascara, and lipstick, will take no more than five to eight minutes. At night or for a special occasion you can spend more time fussing or experimen-ting with your make-up, but for work or every day, it's a snap. So there's no excuse for ever leaving your house without your finished look!

Always apply foundation with a cosmetic sponge. Your fingers can stretch and pull your skin, and the application will be less even. A dry sponge gives a slightly heavier coverage. For a sheerer look, use a sponge that's slightly moist, but not wet.

Remember that all the instructions are summarised in the Beauty Workbook at the back of the book.

*THE STEPS*

**1.** (Optional) Apply colour adjuster with a dry cosmetic sponge. Dot on the areas where needed, then pat and slightly blend with the sponge.

**2.** Dab foundation on the corner of your cosmetic sponge. Avoid dipping your fingers in the bottle, which can contaminate the contents.

**3.** Dot the foundation on your forehead, cheeks, nose, and chin, then smooth it evenly over your entire face with downward and outward strokes. (The hairs on your face grow downwards.) Spread foundation only down to your jawline – the colours of your face and neck never match, so foundation on your neck will show. Blend the foundation carefully along your jawline so there are no rough edges.

**4.** With the corner of your sponge, gently work foundation into the area around your nose and under your eyes. If you don't intend to use eye shadow base, apply foundation to the upper eye area as well.

**5.** Lightly cover your mouth with the leftover foundation on the sponge. Too much foundation on the lips can cause your lipstick to run.

**6.** (Optional) Using your under-eye brush, dab coverstick under your eyes, only on the dark areas. Remember, don't apply coverstick to puffy spots or you'll call attention to them. Use the same method to minimise shadows around your nostrils or the smile lines around your mouth and in the hollow above your chin. Dot the coverstick lightly on your blemishes as well. Blend by patting lightly with your *clean* fingertip. The warmth of your finger will melt the coverstick so the edges will blend, but don't rub or blend it to the point that it disappears.

**7.** (Optional) Place a small dot of eye shadow base on each eyelid and blend it from your lids to your brows, using a sponge or your fingertip. Allow it to set for a moment before you open your eyes.

That's it! You're finished. See how easy it was? Now you have a choice. For a beautiful, basic everyday look, you can skip the following chapter and go on to the next easy step – powder. If, however, you want to spend some extra time learning the art of contouring your face, now's the time to curl up with Chapter 8, 'Face Sculpting'.

# FACE SCULPTING

FACE sculpting is the art of enhancing or minimising sections of your face using the artist's principles of shadow and light to create illusions. Sculpting can slim your nose, minimise a heavy jaw or a double chin, widen your eyes, create high cheekbones, or even give you a temporary 'facelift'.

Sculpting is not for everyone. Some women don't need it and others don't want to fuss that much. And in the daytime, you must use a very light hand, as sculpting can look artificial in daylight. Still, you may want to try it if you're being photographed, appearing on TV, or going out for a glamorous evening.

Sculpting is always done after you apply your foundation and before you brush on powder. The two techniques involved are *highlighting*, or using light to accentuate, and *contouring*, or using shadow to create shape and to minimise.

To highlight you'll need a foundation or a coverstick one or two shades lighter than usual. For evening, you could even use a white or a pearly shade. To contour, you'll use foundation, coverstick, or tinted pressed powder in a shade slightly darker than usual.

For most sculpting illusions, a foundation or a coverstick will be your best choice for contour shades because they're the least obvious and the easiest to use. But for 'lifting' your eyes, you'll need the tinted pressed powder, which you may also prefer for some of the slimming techniques as well. Choose a soft, neutral colour slightly darker than your foundation. In buying a tinted powder, be guided by your season: Cool Winters and Summers should choose a slightly rosy beige; warm-toned Autumns and Springs, a more golden beige. You may have to go to a specialist beauty supply house to find contour powder, as most cosmetic lines don't carry it.

Once you've assembled the proper tools and products, the keys to successful sculpting are a light touch and careful, even blending. In other words, don't overdo it!

Now determine the features you want to sculpt.

## YOUR EYES

Eye sculpting is done on top of your foundation and regular con-cealers, including eye shadow base. To widen and 'lift' your eyes, use your under-eye brush to place a medium-size dot of highlighter at the inner corner of each eye, on each side of the bridge of your nose. Gently press each dot for a few seconds to blend in the highlighter. Next, do the same thing at the outer corner of each eye. (*One exception:* If your eyes are very close together, omit the highlighter at the outside corners.) The highlighter will seem to 'erase' the boundaries of your eyes, making them appear bigger.

To give 'lift' to your eyes, apply *powder* contour shade just above the outside half of your eyebrow, sweeping it up to the hairline (see the drawing opposite). You can use either your blusher brush or your big, fluffy powder brush for a soft effect. You should not see much actual colour, but rather a soft shading that will seem to lift the eye. Follow with your regular eye make-up (see Chapter 11).

## YOUR NOSE

To slim your nose, you will need both your highlighter and your contour shade, as well as a clean under-eye brush. With your highlighter, draw a line down the centre of your nose and pat it with your fingertip to blend lightly. Next, draw a line with your contour shade down each side of your nose, again patting to blend. Make sure you don't leave any rough edges where the contour shade and highlighter meet. Now, to make the tip of your nose more angular, apply a touch of your contour shade in the bevels on either side of the tip of your nose. Finally, take a sponge still damp with your normal foundation and press it gently over your nose to soften the effect.

## YOUR CHEEKS

You don't have to be born with the fashionably high cheekbones so many glamorous models have. Here's how they get them. First, find your cheekbones with your fingertips. With your under-eye brush, dot a line of highlighter along the top edge of each cheekbone up to the hairline, then gently pat with fingertips to blend. Next, take your contour shade and make a similar line of dots along the bottom edge of each cheekbone, in the hollow of your cheek, and blend once again. Now, lightly press your sponge, still damp with your regular foundation, over your cheekbones to soften the sculpting. If you want to intensify the effect, you can lightly dust your tinted contour powder just under your cheekbones, using your fan brush. Later, you will apply blusher to the crest of your cheekbone.

If your cheeks seem sunken or your face too thin, you can 'fill out' this area by applying your highlighter to the area *below* your cheekbone, and omitting it from above. Do not, however, apply the darker contour shade above the cheekbone, as it will make your eyes look sunken.

## *YOUR LIPS*

Many of us have lips that are unbalanced, with one larger or smaller than the other. Here's how to correct the disparity.

First, cover your lips entirely with foundation to erase existing lip boundaries. Then, to bring out a small lip, take a clean under-eye brush and draw a thin line of highlighter along the outer edge of your lip, feathering lightly. To reduce a full lip, draw a similar line with your contour shade. You can also apply your lipstick or lip pencil a *teeny* bit outside your lip line on your thin lip and a bit inside the boundary on your full lip (see page 155). But be subtle. Your balancing shouldn't be noticeable.

After sculpting, follow with lipstick as usual (see Chapter 12).

## *YOUR JAWLINE AND CHIN*

For a wide jaw (one that is broader than your cheekbones) or a bothersome double chin, you can use your contour shade either alone or combined with tinted powder. Simply blend the contour shade along your jawline and underneath your chin. For evening or photography, you may want to add another light brush of tinted powder. If you prefer, you can use the tinted powder alone for softer shading.

These are fun little tricks to play with on a rainy day or when you're in the mood to try for dramatic special effects. For everyday wear, you'll simply dust your foundation with a puff of powder. Read on!

# POWDER

ONCE you've applied your foundation, concealer, and any sculpting products, you're ready for powder, the finishing touch. (If you use a moist blusher, this too will go underneath your powder. We'll get to blusher in the next chapter.)

We need powder for three reasons. First, it removes any tackiness from the foundation, leaving a smooth, dry finish on which to apply blusher. Blusher can 'grab' or streak if applied directly to foundation, especially in hot or humid weather. Second, powder keeps your foundation fresh-looking all day. Third, and best of all, it gives your face a beautiful, matt finish that will bring you compliments on your wonderful complexion. Try powdering just one side of your face to see what a difference it makes!

Today's powder is extremely light and sheer, as far from the cakey kind our grandmothers wore as the mangle is from the spin dryer. It will not accentuate wrinkles and can be applied to the eye area (eyes closed, of course).

Powder is for all skin types. If you're using an oil-free foundation, however, you won't need powder. Oil-free foundations consist of watered talc, so they will dry powdery. Once buffed, you will already have your smooth, matt finish.

## *CHOOSING THE RIGHT COLOUR*

Powder comes in shades similar to foundation colours. You can also buy a colourless, translucent powder suitable for any foundation; it simply disappears into the foundation, even on black skin tones. In addition, you will find powder in tints of pink, peach, lavender, and green, in both matt and iridescent finishes, as well as silver and gold in an iridescent finish only. Matt is for daytime, iridescent for night.

To choose a natural colour, follow the same guidelines as for foundation: a rosy beige tone for the cool Winters and Summers, a golden tone for Autumns and Springs. Colourless, translucent powder, of course, is excellent for all seasons. I prefer it because it looks totally natural and you can't go wrong.

To wear tinted powders, again use your season's palette: pink or silver for the cools, peach or gold for the warms. Green and lavender powders are similar to colour correctors. Lavender is for the sallow skins, green for the ruddies.

## *TYPES OF POWDER*

There are two types of powder: loose and pressed.

**Loose powder** is desirable because it has no oils added to hold it together. It's the powder you will use at home to give you that wonderful, finished look. It applies easily with a fluffy brush or a soft puff, and you can apply as much as you like because any excess will simply brush off.

You can buy loose powder in a boxed container, but my personal preference is a shaker bottle, which allows you to sprinkle out just enough powder for one application into your hand. This method keeps loose powder from sifting all over your dressing table – both a mess and a waste. And because your powder brush touches only the dispensed powder, you never have to worry about adding bacteria to the container.

**Pressed powder** comes in a compact with a puff, is easy to carry with you, and is great for touch-ups. I always keep a compact of translucent pressed powder in my bag for spot touch-ups throughout the day. If you use a compact frequently, make sure you wash your powder puff often to prevent bacteria and oil from building up. Just swirl your puff through warm water and mild soap and then toss it into your tumble dryer.

## APPLYING POWDER

Powder is one step you won't mind adding to your daily routine because it's so quick and easy. You can't make a mistake, and the results are beautiful. Here, we'll apply regular, matt finish powder. You'll learn how to use iridescent powder in Chapter 13.

• To apply loose powder, begin by sprinkling a little powder into the palm of your hand. Dip your brush into the powder and shake off the excess. Then, using downward strokes to smooth your delicate facial hairs, brush the powder lightly on forehead, cheeks, nose, chin, and eyes, in that order. You want most of the powder on your face, less on the eye area. Give your face another light brushing, again with downward strokes, to remove any excess powder.

• To give your face an extra touch of radiance, you can dip your powder brush first in your blusher, then in translucent powder, and stroke over your entire face. The hint of colour adds a special glow.

• To make powder really stay on and keep your foundation 'set' for hours, you can press the powder on with a firm powder puff or dry cosmetic sponge. Dip the puff into the powder and press it on your face, gently patting. Don't rub! Press and pat. If you feel you've overdone it and the powder looks thick, brush the excess off with your fluffy brush.

• To apply pressed powder, you can use a brush or the puff in the compact. Pressed powder tends to get hard, but you can loosen it by scratching a light × on its surface with your brush handle. Apply as with loose powder. To use the puff, simply pat it on where needed, repeating until any facial 'shine' is gone.

Now your canvas is ready, so let's go on to the fun part – adding glorious colour!

CHAPTER · 10

# BLUSHER

NO OTHER cosmetics item gives as immediate a result as blusher. If you have little natural cheek colour, blusher will bring your face to life with a youthful, healthy glow. Even if your cheeks are rosy, blusher will distribute the colour more evenly, as nature tends to centre the rosiness all in front. Blusher comes in a wide range of forms, so you can easily find a type you like. Better yet, blusher is available in a spectrum of colours appropriate for your season.

## CHOOSING THE RIGHT COLOUR

Knowing your season makes it easy to choose a blusher that looks perfect on your skin tone and harmonises with your wardrobe as well. Because you are choosing both blusher and clothing colours from your season's palette, your make-up and wardrobe automatically go together!

You can wear one basic blusher to blend with all your clothes, but you will look even better – and certainly have more fun – if you have several shades to coordinate more precisely with the range of colours in your wardrobe. A Winter can wear pink blusher with her fuchsia blouse, but she will look more harmonious wearing fuchsia blusher.

Autumn's peach blusher will blend with her terracotta blouse, but why not go for the smashing look of terracotta blusher?

Using your season's Make-up Wardrobe Chart in Chapter 4 as a shopping guide, start with a basic, everyday blusher and then add to your collection of shades as your budget allows. Remember, as you are shopping for a particular colour – say, plum or peach, depending on your season – start with a medium colour, and if it's too dark or light, go lighter or darker as needed. Blusher colours are deceiving in the compact, and the colour often looks quite different on your skin.

Here are some guidelines to help keep your shopping organised as you build your blusher wardrobe:

• *Winters:* For your basic colour, look for a clear, medium pink or, if your skin is darkish, a burgundy. Black skins, especially, should consider burgundy their number-one basic. Be sure to choose shades that are true, rather than dulled. Your next blusher purchases might be a soft, true red and a fuchsia, to go with those clothing colours. Last, add a plum to round out your wardrobe needs.

• *Summers:* Start with a soft rose for your first blusher. It's your most flattering shade and one that will match most of your wardrobe. Next, add a soft watermelon red and a soft fuchsia, to go with those special clothing colours. Don't go too bright on the red. You may want to try a cream or liquid rouge, which tends to go on softer than the powdered red blushers. Last, add soft plum to harmonise with your mauve, plum, and burgundy clothes.

• *Autumns:* If your skin is medium to dark, you'll love a tawny peach blusher for your everyday colour; if you are very fair, try a lighter apricot shade. Next, add a salmon for the pinkish side of your wardrobe and a mocha shade to go with your browns and brown burgundy. Last, add a brick red to go with your reds and, depending on your colouring, either a chestnut or a brighter terracotta for your rusts and pumpkins.

• *Springs:* For your first purchase, aim for a clear salmon blusher that's not too pink and not too orange. It's your perfect basic. Then add a peach or an apricot for the orange side of your wardrobe and a warm pink for your pinks. Last, you might get a soft shade of poppy red. Like Summer, you may want to choose a cream or liquid formula for sheer application. Be sure to avoid any brownish or tawny blushers. Spring needs clear colours to look her best.

## CHOOSING THE RIGHT FORMULA

Blusher comes in a range of forms – *powder, cream, gel, liquid,* and *mousse* – and under a variety of names, including *rouge, blusher,* and *cheek tint. Rouge* is usually a cream, *blusher* a powder, and *cheek tint* a gel or liquid. Each of these forms offers certain advantages. Some are especially suited to certain skin types; some are especially easy to apply; and certain types offer sheer coverage, ideal for bright colours. The form that's best for you will depend on a balance of all these factors. Let's look at each type.

**Powder blusher** is the most popular and the easiest to apply. It comes in either a matt or frosted finish. Both matt and slightly frosted blusher are suitable for day wear, but highly frosted blusher is strickly for night.

With modern technology, pressed-powder blusher has become so refined that it glides beautifully on *any* skin type. Look for a brand that feels smooth and silky when you rub it between your fingers. Grainy or chalky blushers will not go on as easily or look as sheer and natural.

Powdered blusher is applied with a blusher brush. Although most powder blushers come in a compact with a brush, you will find that the higher quality, natural hair brush in your at-home brush set (see Chapter 5) will give you the sheerest, smoothest effect. Use the brush in the compact for touch-ups. For most shades, you simply stroke your brush across the blusher, tap off any excess, and apply. The pigments in red and deep-coloured blushers tend to 'grab', however, and you may need to dip your brush in loose powder first, then the blusher, so the colour will stroke on smoothly.

**Cream rouge** is applied with the fingers and is easy to use, but it must be well blended. Because of its fairly high oil content, cream rouge is not recommend for oily or acne-prone skins. Its creamy texture makes it a good choice for the woman with dry skin or one who wants a very subtle wash of colour. You don't have to worry about a cream rouge being too bright, because you can blend it down to almost nothing. Choose a rouge that feels silky, not greasy to the touch.

In the past, cream rouge was often worn under powder blusher to build up colour intensity or to help the powder cling. With the quality of powder blusher today, this is no longer necessary.

Creams come in either subtly frosted or nonfrosted shades. Frosts are best on younger skin (they may accentuate wrinkles) or in the evening to reflect candlelight.

To apply cream blusher, place three or four dots of colour along you cheekbone with your middle fingertip, then gently smooth and 'feather' the blusher with your ring and middle fingers until it is completely blended and no edges show.

**Gels** or **cheek tints** are sheer blushers that come in a tube or a pot and are applied with the fingertips. They are primarily water-based, with little or no oil, so they are best on oily skin. However, because they contain so little oil, they also dry very quickly and can be difficult to apply. You have to dot them on one cheek at a time and blend deftly and quickly to avoid blotching. Mistakes with gels are harder to correct than with any other form of blusher, and they will often stain your skin, making the colour too bright. If the colour is too heavy, go over it with a small amount of foundation on a dry make-up sponge (water will streak a gel), smoothing the entire area. When properly applied, gels have the benefit of looking very sheer and natural and will last for a long time. Gels are usually not frosted.

**Liquid blushers,** also called colour rubs or washes, come in a bottle and are applied with the fingers. Like cream rouge, a liquid blusher is easy to work with and provides sheer coverage. In fact, some of the washes are so sheer that you can use them all over your face for a subtle 'sun-kissed' look. Liquid blushers are best on normal to oily skin.

Liquid blusher comes both frosted and nonfrosted. The frosted shades are often sheer enough to wear even if you're older or have dry skin, and they can give you a fresh, dewy look.

To apply liquid blusher, just dot it along your cheekbones and feather to blend with your fingertips, then smooth over with your cosmetic sponge, blending the edges well.

**Mousses** are sheer, light-textured foams that come in aerosol cans. They are suitable for all skin types, except the very dry. They, too, are applied with the fingers, which can be a tricky job. They tend to run and it's hard to place them properly, especially if too much foam pumps out. It's best to foam a small amount (about the size of a grape) into the palm of your hand. Then, using your fingertips, apply it thinly to dot and smooth it along your cheekbone. Blend the edges with a dry cosmetic sponge. If you want more intense colour, apply a second coat rather than try to use a large dollop. Once you've learned to control them, mousses are natural-looking. They are not frosted and, once dry, can be blended at the edges with your contour brush.

To decide which blusher formula is best for you, try on the testers at your local department store and see which are easiest for you to apply and which one feels best on your skin. If you're a true novice, buy a powdered blusher. You can't go wrong. If you choose any of the moist blushers – cream, liquid, gel, or mousse – you will need to apply them directly on *top* of your foundation, *before* applying powder. Then follow with powder.

## *INGREDIENTS AND SENSITIVITIES*

The primary ingredient in powder blusher is talc, which is combined with colouring agents, preservatives, fragrance (sometimes), and oils and wax before it is pressed into form. Frosted blusher includes mica or sometimes ground pearl to give it a shiny, smooth finish. Some powder blushers contain pure silk or cornsilk to smooth their application, but how smooth a blusher feels is determined mainly by the degree of processing that the blusher receives, rather than its ingredients.

Cream blusher contains the same ingredients as powdered blusher, but in different proportions – more oil and less talc. Liquids, gels, and mousses are water-based and tend to contain glycerin, or a similar substance, rather than oils, to make them spreadable.

Read the ingredients on the label to judge the oil or water content of the product. Remember, the ingredients are listed in order of predominance. Acne-prone skin will want to avoid mineral oil, unless it's one of the last ingredients in a powder blusher. As with foundation, you will want to avoid isopropyl myristate, which may aggravate acne. Sensitive skins should avoid products containing fragrance or a high amount of lanolin. Sometimes a particular dye or preservative can cause a reaction. If your skin reacts to a product, you will have to be your own detective and try different brands and read labels until you catch the offending ingredient.

Be careful not to apply blusher products near your eyes. Ask at the beauty counter whether the blusher is safe for use on the eyes. It can be dangerous!

## APPLYING BLUSHER

Once you've found a blusher you like in your ideal basic colour, you can quickly learn to apply it. The secret to a natural and flattering look is in the intensity and the placement.

As a rule of thumb, always apply just a little more blusher than you think you need. The blusher will look less bright once you've balanced it with eye make-up and lip colour. And if you wish, you can always go back and adjust it. If your blusher seems too bright, powder it or remove a little with your contour brush or a cosmetic sponge. If it's too pale, add a touch more. Balance is the key.

When wearing a brightly coloured outfit, you may want to apply two shades of blusher. First apply a soft colour, and then dab a more vivid shade right on the crest of your cheekbone. You will get the intensity you need, but still look natural.

The right placement of your blusher is just as important as the intensity. Applying blusher too low can make your face look droopy. If you apply it too high, into the circles under your eye, you'll look as if someone punched you! Flattering placement is easy to achieve if you follow these simple guidelines.

## THE STEPS

**1.** Looking directly into a mirror, apply blusher along the cheekbone, starting right under the outer edge of your iris. You can find this spot by placing two fingers next to your nose – start there, outside your fingers. Blend the colour out to the hairline at the tip of your ear. Most of the colour should be on the crest of the bone, approximately at the outer corner of your eye.

**2.** Feather the colour slightly downwards into the hollow of your cheek, in a tear-drop shape, but:

• *Don't* go lower than the centre of your ear at the outside, or below your nose on the inside.

• *Don't* go closer to your nose than the outer edge of your iris.

• *Don't* go into the circular area under your eye.

• *Don't* go as high as your temple.

These are foolproof boundaries for proper placement!

*Note:* If you used a contour shade in the hollow of your cheek, as in Chapter 8, then apply the blusher just along the top of your cheekbone, blending downwards into the contour shade.

**3.** Using your contour brush, which is slightly stiff, blend all edges so there is no distinct line where your blusher ends.

Do not forget that if you have a narrow face you can use your blusher to make it look wider. Likewise, careful use of blusher can make it look narrower.

## FACE SHAPING

*If your face is quite narrow, you can widen its appearance by starting the blusher at the outer corner of your eye and blending the colour straight back to the hairline at the centre of your ear.*

*If your face is wide, slim its appearance by blending the blusher slightly more upwards toward the hairline just above each ear, and bringing it just a smidge lower than your nose, at the other end. You may also apply your blusher in a wider band than those with narrow or average faces.*

Using your Beauty Workbook at the back of the book as a guide, keep practising until you get it just right. Before long you'll be able to apply your blusher in seconds. You'll look great, and that's a happy way to start the day!

CHAPTER · 11

# EYES

AKE-UP has been enhancing beautiful eyes for aeons; anthropologists think that the cavemen discovered copper and other metals in their quest for dramatic eye shadow. Cleopatra was famous for her glamorous eyes, as are the more recent beauties, Elizabeth Taylor, Sophia Loren and Twiggy, all with magnificent eyes.

Although eye make-up is easy to apply, many women find it more intimidating than any other cosmetic. Most are comfortable with mascara and perhaps even a little eyeliner, but eye shadow is a puzzle. I didn't wear eye shadow for years, because I wasn't sure what colour to buy, where to put it, or even why I should wear it. Now I'm a devotee. There is a vast difference between 'natural' eyes with no make-up and 'natural-looking' eyes with skillfully applied make-up. On the one hand, you are ignoring your eyes; on the other, you are enhancing their natural beauty! So let's make you famous for your beautiful eyes, too.

The purpose of eye make-up is threefold: to focus attention on your eyes by giving them definition; to accentuate the colour of your eyes through flattering colour choices; and to enhance the shape of your eyes through contouring. To accomplish these goals, eye make-up includes four different kinds of products: *eye shadow, eye liner, eyebrow definer*, and *mascara*. They come in various forms and colours, and work together to create a look you will love.

Here we will learn a basic, natural look – one you can use for ever. As with clothing, eye make-up fashions come and go, but a polished, natural, attractive look will always be in style.

## CHOOSING THE RIGHT COLOURS

Knowing your season helps you select your perfect eye colours from the vast array of choices available at cosmetics counters. Eye products come in neutral shades as well as 'colour colours'. Neutrals – the browns and greys – are the easiest to handle, and look natural. Generally, Winters and Summers should look for the cooler silver greys and blue-greys, or browns that have a greyish or cocoa tinge. Autumns and Springs will be flattered by warm browns, ones with hints of honey, gold, or copper, or yellow-greys.

For everyday wear, many women will prefer neutrals, always tasteful and almost foolproof to apply. But you can have fun with colours, too, and they can look nearly as natural as neutrals as long as they're applied with a light hand and are well blended. There is a vast, almost awesome array of colours available today – vibrant and discreet; intense and pale; matts, frosts, iridescents, and even shadows with metallic glints. Matt or slightly frosted shades are your choices for daytime, with the sparkly ones reserved for night.

To sort through the wealth of make-up colours and find the ones best for you, begin by considering your season:

- *Winters* and *Summers*, look for *cool* shades, the ones similar to your wardrobe colours. Cool shades include taupe, pink, lavender, grape, purple, steel blue, navy, spruce green, mint, charcoal, and silver, in addition to your cool greys and browns.

- *Autumns* and *Springs*, choose *warm* shades, like your clothing colours. Warm shades include ivory, peach, warm pink, sage green, olive green, yellow-green, warm violet, bronze, copper, and gold, plus your honey and coffee browns and yellow-greys.

- *Universal colours* are champagne, aqua, teal blue, teal green, and periwinkle blue. These shades are on the border of both warm and cool and will blend with all the seasons' skin tones (but not necessarily with all eye colours, which we will discuss below). Another versatile colour is turquoise, but I have included it only on the Winter and Autumn charts because it can be too dark for Spring and Summer.

Practise recognising warm and cool eye shadow colours. If you line up six different shades of green eye shadow, you'll see that some are warm, such as olive, sage and golden green; and others, such as spruce and mint (harder to find, by the way), are cool, devoid of a yellow cast. Go back to the make-up palettes on pages 31 to 37 and take a look at each season's green. See what a difference the undertone makes? Then look again at the eye colour illustration on page 140.

Now that you know your range of shades, you need to consider the colour of your eyes. The rule here is that make-up must either *match* or *contrast* with your eye colour. Aqua blue eye make-up may be a fine choice, judging by your season alone, but if your eyes are greyish blue, it will clash. Instead of enhancing the beautiful colour of your eyes, the mismatched blue will look garish. A steel blue closer to your eye colour will be much more flattering. Similarly, yellow-green eyes need warm greens and olives, rather than blue green. Rose brown eyes need taupes and cocoa rather than bronze or coppery shades. Try a little dab of eye shadow on your lid, just above the iris. Don't blend it. Just see if the colour clashes or blends with your eye colour. If it doesn't match, try another shade. Now you see why there are so many different varieties of blues, greens, and browns!

Contrasting colours are much easier to select than matching colours. Grape, violet, and purple, for example, will harmonise with blue, green, and brown eyes alike. Brown eyes can wear the most shades well because brown is itself a neutral colour. The Eye Make-up Charts on pages 127 to 130 list your colour options according to both your season *and* your eye colour. You will want to experiment with shades to find your favourites.

With your colours in mind, let's look at the types of eye make-up you'll need. A basic wardrobe includes at least *one eyeliner* or *eye pencil, two or three shades of eye shadow*, and *one mascara*. You may also want to buy an *eyebrow definer* if your brows need filling in. We'll consider each item in turn, with the appropriate colours.

## Eyeliners and Pencils

Eyeliners and pencils are used for definition. They make your eyes stand out and help your eyelashes appear wonderfully full and thick. You may be accustomed to black eyeliner, but many more shades are open to you and may, in fact, be more complementary. Neutrals look the most natural, but you can also try colours that match or complement your eyes, especially for evening. It often looks great to line your lower lid with a neutral, and your upper lid with a colour similar to your eye shadow.

Select a colour that is similar in intensity to the colour of your eyes, lashes, and brows. If you are a blonde Summer, say, with pale skin and blue eyes, the black or charcoal liner that brunette Winters can wear will be too harsh on you. You'll want to select a lighter shade – maybe a medium grey or slate blue – in the same cool range. By the same token, if you are an Autumn with dark coppery hair and deep brown eyes, pale sage green eyeliner will disappear on you. You'll need a deeper green or brown to offset your vivid colouring.

### Eye Shadows

Eye shadows enhance both the colour and the shape of your eyes, making them seem larger, more expressive, even dramatic. Once you know how to use shadows, you'll probably enjoy them more than any other make-up you wear. Because they come in such a wide array of colours, they offer the greatest potential for creativity.

Your first purchases will be a *highlighter* and one or two *contour shadows*. The highlighter is used to lighten and bring out areas; the contour shade is used to recess and reshape areas. If you have a lid that barely shows, for example, you will put highlighter on the lid. If the bony area above your eye is prominent, you will apply a contour shade there, to push the area back and give the illusion of a larger eye. We'll discuss how and where to apply these shadows later in this chapter.

For your basic, everyday look, purchase fairly neutral colours that flatter your eye colour. These will go with everything in your wardrobe automatically. As you get more comfortable with eye shadow, you can add shades to your collection, to blend with the colours in your wardrobe. Just remember that you never want to add a colour – regardless of your clothing – that doesn't flatter your eyes.

Again, the intensity of your eye shadow should be based on your colouring. You don't want to look garish with a colour that's too bright or dark, or over-subtle in a colour that disappears. A deep teal may be fine for a dark-haired Autumn, but a pale aqua shade will be better for a blonde, fair Spring.

The Eye Make-up Charts will show you some attractive highlighter and contour colour choices for your season. Combining the shadow colours is relatively easy, because your choices all come from your colour palette of harmonious colours. You might, for example, combine a pink highlighter with grape and purple contour shades, or a pale grey highlighter with medium grey and steel blue shadows, if you are a cool season. Warm seasons can combine peach highlighter with copper and brown shadows, or ivory with medium brown and teal. Now is your chance to experiment and be creative. Some of your most surprising combinations may turn out to be your favourites. (One of mine is grape and teal.) Just remember to blend the colours well!

## Mascara

Mascara colours and plumps up your lashes to make them look long and luxuriant. The basic shades are the neutrals – black, brown-black, and brown – but navy, forest, spruce, and olive can look natural, too, because they dry dark. Black is best for Winters and darker Autumns; brown-black for darker-haired Springs and Summers; and brown for lighter Autumns, Springs, and Summers. You can try navy if you have blue or brown eyes; forest, spruce, or olive if your eyes are green or brown.

Brighter-coloured mascaras are in vogue today, but they will undoubtedly be gone tomorrow. Though neutrals are a must for a well-groomed office look, the brighter colours, if used with care, can be fun for the young or the young at heart. Teal, aqua, violet, and other vivid shades can be applied to the entire lash or just to the lash tips. I like them best worn over a neutral, as a faint second coat, giving just a hint of colour when the light hits your lashes. If you want to try coloured mascaras, choose ones in shades that match your eye shadows.

## Eyebrow Definers

Don't buy an eyebrow definer unless you really need it to feather in bare spots or to even the length of your brows. Not only are heavily drawn brows out of fashion, but your eyes will look larger if your brows are not too dark. Sophia Loren, for example, early in her career had dark, heavy brows (look at some of her early pictures), but over time she began to bleach them to a slightly lighter shade, and her intense, beautiful eyes really came to life.

If you decide you need an eyebrow definer, choose one that closely matches your brows and blends with the colour of your hair. Test the colour by drawing a line on your forehead – it's the best way to see if a colour has any hidden tints, such as red, that might clash with your colouring. Summer or Winter blondes should look for taupes without any red tones, while Autumn and Spring blondes should choose light golden browns. If you're a Winter or Summer with darker hair and brows, try cool cocoa or charcoal browns; the warmer reddish or golden browns are for the redheaded or brunette Autumns and

Springs. If your brows are grey, try taupe or a light grey pencil; if your brows are truly black, you can use a charcoal pencil.

## *THE EYE MAKE-UP CHARTS*

The following Eye Make-up Charts summarise your colour choices. After you see which colours are best for you, according to both your season and your eye colour, go back to your season's Make-up Wardrobe Chart in Chapter 4 and cross off any eye shadow suggestions that won't harmonise with your eye colour. In other words, every colour listed on your Make-up Wardrobe Chart won't necessarily suit you, even if it suits your clothes. For example, if you have Autumn green eyes and decide to wear a teal blue blouse, you cannot wear teal blue eye shadow because it will clash with your green eyes. Instead, wear a teal green or a green that blends with your eyes, or wear one of your brown or copper shadows. These will complement both your blouse and your eyes.

You will usually have to try on several versions of an eye shadow colour to find the intensity that's right for you. For example, a grape shade in one brand may go on very dark, while another brand's grape may look soft and light when applied. You can't always tell by the way the colour appears in the container. I've seen a teal that looks ultra bright in the pan go on the skin so softly you can barely see it. Try the colours on – it's the only way to tell if one is right for you.

Note, too, that some eye shadow colours blend into the skin so they look almost as neutral as brown or grey, while other shadows remain more 'colourful'. On the chart, I have marked the more neutral shades with an (N), to help you make your selection. In addition, some highlighters are very pale and blend into the skin, so they barely show. You don't really see colour; they simply lighten the area. Other highlighters have a bit more colour, and you can see a tint of green, pink, blue, or peach when they are applied. To differentiate between the two, I like to call the brighter highlighters 'uplifters', because in small amounts they lift and brighten areas of the eye. Uplifters are usually too colourful to use on the entire eye area, but a dash applied just under the arch of the brow or in the centre of the lid can add a wonderful touch of 'light' to these special spots. I've marked the uplifters with a (U).

## WINTER EYE MAKE-UP CHART

| Eye Colour | Blue | Green Hazel | Brown |
|---|---|---|---|
| **Highlighters** | Champagne<br>Pale Grey<br>Taupe<br>Pale Pink<br>Pale Yellow<br>Cool Pink (U)<br>Cool Blue (U) or<br>Aqua (U)<br>Light Lavender (U)<br>Mauve (U)<br>Silver (U) | Champagne<br>Pale Grey<br>Taupe<br>Pale Pink<br>Pale Yellow<br>Cool Pink (U)<br>Mint (U)<br>Mauve (U)<br>Silver (U) | Champagne<br>Pale Grey<br>Taupe<br>Pale Pink<br>Pale Yellow<br>Pink (U)<br>Mint (U)<br>Aqua (U)<br>Mauve (U)<br>Silver (U) |
| **Contour Shades** | Cocoa (N)<br>Cool Grey (N)<br>Greyed Purple (N)<br>Navy (N)<br>Steel Blue (N) or<br>*Teal Blue (N)<br>Purple<br>Sapphire<br>Periwinkle Blue | Cocoa (N)<br>Cool Grey (N)<br>Greyed Purple (N)<br>Navy (N)<br>*Teal Green (N) or<br>Spruce Green (N)<br>Purple | Cocoa (N)<br>Cool Grey (N)<br>Greyed Purple (N)<br>Steel Blue (N)<br>Navy (N)<br>Spruce Green (N)<br>Purple<br>Sapphire<br>*Teal Blue<br>*Teal Green |
| **Liners** | Black (N)<br>Charcoal Grey (N)<br>Navy (N)<br>Deep Purple<br>Periwinkle Blue<br>Steel Blue or<br>*Teal Blue<br>(best match with<br>eye colour) | Black (N)<br>Charcoal Grey (N)<br>Spruce Green (N)<br>Deep Purple | Black (N)<br>Charcoal Grey (N)<br>Navy (N)<br>Spruce Green (N)<br>Deep Purple<br>*Teal Blue |

*Note that Teal Blue or Teal Green will look like a 'colour' on a brown eye, but more neutral on blue or green eyes.*

## SUMMER EYE MAKE-UP CHART

| Eye Colour | Blue | Green Hazel | Brown |
|---|---|---|---|
| **Highlighters** | Champagne<br>Pale Pink<br>Pale Grey<br>Pale Yellow<br>Cool Blue (U) or<br>Aqua (U)<br>Cool Pink (U)<br>Light Lavender (U)<br>Mauve (U)<br>Silver (U) | Champagne<br>Pale Pink<br>Pale Grey<br>Pale Yellow<br>Mint Green (U)<br>Cool Pink (U)<br>Light Lavender (U)<br>Mauve (U)<br>Silver (U) | Champagne<br>Pale Pink<br>Pale Grey<br>Pale Yellow<br>Aqua (U)<br>Cool Pink (U)<br>Mint (U)<br>Mauve (U)<br>Silver (U) |
| **Contour Shades** | Cocoa (N)<br>Silvered Mauve (N)<br>Cool Grey (N)<br>Grape (N)<br>Steel Blue (N) or<br>*Teal Blue (N)<br>Periwinkle Blue<br>Lavender | Cocoa (N)<br>Silvered Mauve (N)<br>Cool Grey (N)<br>Grape (N)<br>*Teal Green (N)<br>Spruce Green<br>Lavender | Cocoa (N)<br>Silvered Mauve (N)<br>Cool Grey (N)<br>Steel Blue (N)<br>Grape (N)<br>Spruce Green (N)<br>*Teal Green<br>*Teal Blue<br>Periwinkle Blue |
| **Liners** | Navy (N)<br>Medium Grey (N)<br>Charcoal Grey (N)<br>Steel Blue (N) or<br>*Teal Blue<br>  (best match with<br>  eye colour)<br>Amethyst<br>Periwinkle Blue | Medium Grey (N)<br>Charcoal Grey (N)<br>Taupe Brown (N)<br>Spruce Green (N)<br>Amethyst | Medium Grey (N)<br>Charcoal Grey (N)<br>Taupe Brown (N)<br>Navy (N)<br>Spruce Green (N)<br>Amethyst<br>*Teal Blue |

*Teal Blue and Teal Green will look like neutrals on blue or green eyes, but will appear more colourful on a brown eye.

## AUTUMN EYE MAKE-UP CHART

| Eye Colour | Brown | Green Hazel | Blue |
|---|---|---|---|
| **Highlighters** | Champagne<br>Ivory<br>Pale Peach<br>Pale Golden<br> Yellow<br>Peach (U)<br>Light Warm<br> Green (U)<br>Aqua (U)<br>Gold (U) | Champagne<br>Beige<br>Pale Peach<br>Pale Golden<br> Yellow<br>Peach (U)<br>Light Warm<br> Green (U)<br>Gold (U) | Champagne<br>Ivory<br>Pale Peach<br>Pale Golden<br> Yellow<br>Peach (U)<br>Aqua (U)<br>Light Violet (U)<br>Gold (U) |
| **Contour Shades** | Coffee Brown (N)<br>Olive Green (N)<br>Sage (N)<br>Mink (N)<br>Bronze (N)<br>Copper<br>*Teal Blue (N)<br>Teal Green<br>Warm Green | Teal Green or<br>Warm Green or<br>Olive Green (N)<br>Sage Green (N)<br>Coffee Brown (N)<br>Golden Brown (N)<br>Putty (Warm<br> Grey) (N)<br>Bronze (N)<br>Copper | Coffee Brown (N)<br>Golden Brown (N)<br>*Teal Blue (N) or<br>Putty (Warm Grey)<br> (N)<br>Bronze (N)<br>Copper<br>Periwinkle Blue |
| **Liners** | Brown (N)<br>Olive Green (N)<br>Forest Green (N)<br>*Teal Blue (N)<br>*Marine Navy | Brown (N)<br>Forest Green (N)<br>or Olive Green (N)<br> (best match with<br> eye colour)<br>Teal Green | Brown (N)<br>*Marine Navy (N) or<br>*Teal Blue (best<br> match with eye<br> colour)<br>Violet<br>Turquoise |

*Teal Blue or Marine Navy will look neutral on a blue eye, more colourful on a brown eye.*

## SPRING EYE MAKE-UP CHART

| Eye Colour | Blue | Green | Brown Topaz |
|---|---|---|---|
| **Highlighters** | Champagne<br>Ivory<br>Pale Peach<br>Warm Pink<br>Pale Golden<br>  Yellow<br>Peach (U)<br>Aqua (U)<br>Light Violet (U)<br>Gold (U) | Champagne<br>Ivory<br>Pale Peach<br>Warm Pink<br>Pale Golden Yellow<br>Peach (U)<br>Light Warm Green<br>  (U)<br>Gold (U) | Champagne<br>Ivory<br>Pale Peach<br>Pale Golden<br>  Yellow<br>Peach (U)<br>Light Warm Green<br>  (U)<br>Aqua (U)<br>Gold (U) |
| **Contour Shades** | Honey (N)<br>Golden Brown (N)<br>Clear Warm Grey<br>  (N)<br>*Teal Blue (N)<br>Periwinkle Blue<br>Bronze (N)<br>Light Copper<br>Violet | Honey (N)<br>Golden Brown (N)<br>Sage Green (N) or<br>*Teal Green (N) or<br>Warm Green<br>Bronze (N)<br>Light Copper | Honey (N)<br>Golden Brown (N)<br>Bronze (N)<br>Sage Green (N)<br>*Teal Green<br>Light Copper<br>Warm Green |
| **Liners** | *Teal Blue (N) or<br>Turquoise or<br>Slate Blue (N)<br>  (best match with<br>  eye colour)<br>Brown (N)<br>Light Brown (N)<br>Periwinkle<br>Violet | Brown (N)<br>*Teal Green or<br>Olive Green (N) or<br>Sage Green (N)<br>  (best match)<br>Violet | Brown (N)<br>Olive Green (N)<br>*Teal Blue<br>*Teal Green<br>Turquoise |

*Teal Blue and Teal Green look more neutral on blue or green eyes, more colourful on a brown eye.*

## CHOOSING THE RIGHT FORMULA

Before you set out to purchase your eye make-up, you'll want to consider the various forms available.

### Eyeliner

Eyeliner comes in a *pencil*, *liquid*, or *powder* form. I prefer the pencil as it is made of wax and oil and can be 'smudged' to look soft and natural. Be sure to choose one that is creamy so it won't pull the delicate tissue around your eyes. The drawback to pencils is that the colour can run in hot weather, and they are too thick for women with very sparse eyelashes.

Liquids, applied with a brush, stay on well, but tend to create a harsh, continuous line that can be difficult to keep thin and straight. The key to success with liquid liner is choosing a colour that is not too dark, and applying with a thin, good-quality eyeliner brush. Liquids work especially well for women with crepiness on the lids.

You can also use powdered eye shadow to line your eyes. Apply it with a thin, moistened eyeliner brush. It dries to a soft, powdery line that can be blended with a dry under-eye brush. (You can also draw the line with dry eye shadow powder and a dry eyeliner brush. It won't stay on as long, but will look extremely natural.) In warm or humid weather, eye shadow can be the best choice for eyeliner, as it doesn't contain much oil and won't melt from heat. Moistened, it is also an excellent choice for women with crepiness on the lids or women with sparse lashes. The thin brush places the liner close to the lashes, and the 'powdery' line looks natural.

### Eye Shadow

Eye shadows come in *pressed powder* form, as well as in *creams*, *liquids* and *crayons*. Some of the new crayons are called *powder crayons*, containing the same ingredients as pressed powders but moulded into the shape of a fat crayon.

Shadows come in matt, frosted and iridescent formulas. Matt or lightly frosted types are best for daytime; frosts or iridescents for evening. Unless you're very young, you should avoid highly frosted shadows entirely, as they accentuate crepiness.

**Powdered shadows** are the most popular and easiest to control. Their talc base is mixed with oils so they glide smoothly on all skin types. As with blusher, the shadow should feel silky, never chalky or grainy, when you rub it between your fingers. Powdered shadows are applied with a brush or an eye sponge. The brush is used for lighter application and for general blending, the sponge for heavier coverage and for blending stubborn edges.

**Cream shadows** are sometimes preferred by women with dry or ageing skin, since they contain more wax and oil and will minimise crepiness. Creams are not recommended for oily skin, as the colour tends to slip off and collect in the crease of the eye.

Usually applied with the fingertips, creams can be hard to place correctly and blend evenly. Even the types that come in a tube with a wand are difficult to control. If you like cream shadows, try dotting them on with your fingertip, the tip of the wand, or a clean under-eye brush and then blending them with a dry eye shadow brush to place them more precisely and smooth the edges.

**Eye crayons,** whether creamy or powdered, can be 'drawn' on and then blended with a clean, dry eye shadow brush or your stiffer contour brush. They are easy to control, and the powdered ones blend especially well. I don't recommend using the creamy eye crayons on a daily basis, because you must apply a fair amount of pressure to spread them with your brush, and the tugging can stretch your skin, encouraging wrinkles.

### Mascara

There are *liquid*, *cake*, and *cream* mascaras. Liquid is the most popular and comes in regular, water-resistant, and waterproof forms. Regular mascara is fine, but it will run if your eyes water. I like the water-resistant type the best. It won't streak off during aerobics class, yet can be removed easily, even with soap and water. Waterproof mascara is best reserved for the beach or special occasions, as it makes your lashes very stiff and can be removed only with a special make-up solvent. (However, if your bottom lashes tend to smudge easily, which they do on women with short lashes that grow close to the skin, waterproof mascara on the lowers is worth the extra trouble.)

Liquid mascara is easy to apply. It comes in a tube with a wand that often has a little brush on the end to help separate the lashes as you stroke it on. Some liquid mascaras, called *lash builders*, have added nylon or rayon fibres that cling to your lashes, making them look thicker. They're great if your eyes aren't sensitive or you don't wear contact lenses. Otherwise, the little fibres can be irritating.

Cake mascara comes in a little compact and is applied with a wet brush similar to a tiny toothbrush. Because these are water-based, they run very easily. Creams come in a tube, similar to toothpaste, only smaller. They are applied with a tiny brush also, but the cream is messy and harder to control than liquids and cakes. Creams do, however, give your lashes a soft, silky look.

## Eyebrow Definers
Eyebrow colour comes in pencil or pressed-powder form. The powders are especially nice because they feather on with a tiny, stiff brush for a soft, natural look. If you prefer a pencil, be sure to keep the point short and sharp so you can apply it lightly.

## INGREDIENTS AND SENSITIVITIES

Eye shadows contain almost the same ingredients as blushers, but with different coloured pigments. In addition, shadows exclude any ingredients dangerous to the eyes, such as coal tar dyes. As with blusher, the powdered products are primarily talc, with wax and oil; the creams and liquids have more oil, less talc.

Of all your make-up, eye products are the most likely to trigger allergies or irritations. If your make-up is bothering your eyes, first look to your mascara and then to the shadows and liners. Avoid using each product in turn for a day or two, and if you find that the problem subsides, try replacing the offender with one from a hypo-allergenic line.

The additives most likely to spark reactions are fragrances (which most eye products avoid), preservatives, and cosmetic detergents, as well as certain colourants and oils. Sensitive eyes should also avoid 'lash-building' mascaras that have added synthetic fibres.

Be aware that some irritations are caused by you. You must keep your eye make-up and applicators clean. Never use a mascara for longer than six months, as it is the product most likely to breed bacteria. If your eyes are sensitive, avoid putting colour near your tear ducts, the part of the eye most susceptible to irritation. And don't line the rims of your eyes inside your lower lashes. It is easy to scratch and irritate your eye, and the waxes and oils can settle into the socket of your eyeball.

Note, too, that not all problems stem from eye make-up. One friend of mine wasted two weeks looking for the cause of her suddenly swollen and puffy eyes. She spent a small fortune on new brands of eye shadow, but it seemed that she was allergic to all of them. After much discomfort and expense, she finally found the culprit – her eye make-up remover.

Spring pollens and summer grass can make your eyes extra-sensitive, red, and itchy. If you suffer from hay fever and other seasonal allergies, give your eyes a rest from eye make-up for a few days during the especially bad periods.

## APPLYING EYE MAKE-UP

Now you've assembled your eyeliner, highlighting and contour shadows, mascara, and eyebrow definer, if you need one, and you're ready to learn to apply them. Your eyes should be prepared, as we discussed in the chapter on foundation, with eye shadow base or foundation. Expect some exciting results!

Start by evaluating your eyes in the mirror. Can you see the lid, or is it completely hidden when your eyes are open? Visually divide your eyes into two parts – the lid and the brow/orbital bone. Your crease is the dividing line. There are the two areas where you will apply shadows or highlighters to contour your eyes. See if you have more brow, more lid, or approximately equal amounts of each. As when contouring your face, you'll be using light shades to accentuate some areas and medium to dark shades to downplay others. Wherever you have the most room, you'll apply the contour shade; wherever you have the least area, the lighter shade. In all cases, you'll want to add definition to the outer corners of your eyes.

Study your eyes carefully so that in the steps that follow you can determine the most flattering placements for your make-up. While there are endless variations on eye shapes, I have found that the following four types of eyes are most common:

**Proportioned: Lid and brow area approximately equal.** On the proportioned eye, the lid and brow bone are balanced. Usually you have a bit more brow area than lid, but the lid shows. Here you will highlight under the arch of your brow, contour the shape of your orbital bone above the crease, and use a soft shade on your lid to enhance your eye colour. If you have a lot of lid that shows *and* a lot of brow area, you'll follow the same principles, but you won't use bright colours.

**Little or no lid showing, more brow area.** This type of eye has little or no lid showing, with a wider brow area. Asian eyes should consider themselves in this category, as should those with hooded eyes or prominent orbital bones. You will apply a pale highlighter to the lid to bring it out and a darker contour shade above the crease to help create balance.

**Little or no lid showing; small brow area.** This eye has very little space on which to apply eye make-up. On this type of eye you will apply a light shade on both the lid and the brow area. Your goal is to visually expand the area between your eye and eyebrow.

**Prominent lid; small brow area.** Here a lot of lid shows and is often a larger area than the brow bone. You will use a medium neutral shade on the lid to push it back and 'expose' more of the iris, and a paler colour on the brow and orbital bone to lift and open that area.

## *STEP 1: EYELINER*

First, you'll apply your eyeliner, to define your eyes and to make them appear larger. You apply liner before eye shadow for two reasons. First, a creamy eye pencil won't go on smoothly over powdered eye shadow. Second, the application of eye shadow will help to soften and blend the liner, for a more natural look.

With a freshly sharpened pencil (or with liquid liner or moistened powder eye shadow) draw a thin line, as close to the base of the lashes as possible. Try to colour in between the lashes so they'll look thick and luscious. Be careful not to pull or stretch the delicate skin around your eye. If your eye pencil is too hard or dry, swish it across the heat of your blow drier for a second or two, and it will become creamy.

**For the proportioned eye,** line the outer half of your upper and lower lids, feathering a smaller amount of liner towards the nose, to prevent the line ending abruptly. Emphasising the outer half will 'widen' your eyes. Some proportioned eyes have a lot of lid showing, as well as lots of brow. Use a neutral, rather than a bright colour on this type of lid.

**If little or no lid shows** and you have either a large or small brow area, line the entire lower lid, to emphasise the bottom of your eye, but line only the outer third of your upper lid, to keep it 'open' and make your eye look bigger. Lining the upper lid will close in your eye.

**If your lid is prominent** and you have a small brow area, line the entire upper lid almost to the tear duct, to recess the lid a bit, but line only the outer third of your lower lid, feathering the edge so it doesn't end abruptly. Use a medium neutral, rather than a dark or bright colour. Then blend the line to soften it. Be subtle. Everything shows on your type of lid.

Now blend. Work the edges of your liner with an eye sponge or a clean under-eye brush until they grow soft and fuzzy. If the brush seems to spread out the liner too much, try the sponge, which will remove any excess. (A cotton bud works, too.) What you're aiming for is a natural look – a barely perceptible rim of liner.

*Proportioned lid and brow*

*Small lid, small brow*

*Small lid, large brow*

*Large lid, small brow*

## EYE SHAPES

### PROPORTIONED LID AND BROW

*Example: Spring blue eye*

*Cover the entire area with highlighter. Then, apply a contour shade to the orbital bone, a deeper shade to the outer corner of the lid, a pale shade to the inner lid, and for evening, a vertical stripe of uplifter above the iris.*

### LARGE LID; SMALL BROW

*Example: Autumn green eye*

*Apply a medium neutral shade to the entire lid, and accentuate the corner of the lid with a deeper shade. Apply a highlighter to the brow area; then, sweep the deeper shade from the outer corner up onto the orbital bone. Finally, apply an uplifter to the crest of the orbital bone.*

## EYE SHAPES

### SMALL LID; LARGE BROW

*Example: Summer blue eye*

*Apply highlighter to the entire area and then a darker shade on the orbital bone, bringing it high in the centre. Accentuate the outer corner of the eye with a deep shadow, and bring out the lid with a touch of pale colour above the iris.*

### SMALL LID; SMALL BROW

*Example: Winter brown eye*

*Apply a pale colour from lashes to brow. Contour the corner with a deeper shade on the outer third of the lid, swept slightly up towards the outer half of the eyebrow. Do not contour the orbital bone.*

# CHOOSING EYE SHADOW COLOURS

RIGHT                                              WRONG

*A cool blue eye is enhanced by a similar shade of blue eye shadow but clashes with teal blue shadow, even though the highlighter is correct (as in all the example).*

*Yellow-green eyes stand out with champagne highlighter and warm, yellow-green eye shadows but recede and look clownish with blue-green eye shadow.*

*A golden brown eye looks best with golden brown and beige shadows but clashes with rose-brown eye shadow.*

Set your liner by applying the same colour of powdered eye shadow on top of it to keep it from smudging. (If you used black liner, set it with one of your dark eye shadows.) Do this with a clean under-eye brush, turned sideways to get a thinner line. You can skip this step if you used moistened eye shadow powder as your eye liner.

**Special tip for sparse lashes:** If you have few or no eyelashes, you cannot use an eye pencil. No matter how sharp, the pencil will create a line that will be too thick and obvious. Instead, dampen your tiny eyeliner brush and run it across a neutral shade of pressed eye shadow. Choose a colour that is not too dark. Dot the colour along the base of your eyelashes, rather than drawing a solid line. You just want to give your eyes a little definition. When dry, blend slightly with a clean under-eye brush turned sideways.

## STEP 2: EYE SHADOW

Here is your chance to shape and lift your eyes, creating balance and proportion.

**1.** Using your eye sponge, cover your entire eye area, from upper lashes to brows, with a matt or very slightly frosted highlighter. *If your lid is prominent*, don't apply highlighter on the lid; apply it only on the brow area down to the crease. You don't want to bring out the lid any more. For now, just leave it natural, with the foundation or eye shadow base. (See illustration A on page 142.)

**2.** With your angle brush, apply a dark to medium contour colour on the outer third of your lid, almost in the shape of a triangle. Tap excess powder off your brush before applying, so the colour won't 'grab' and be too dark. This colour can be neutral or more colourful, as it won't show much when your eye is open. Here's where you can have fun with colours. *If your lid is prominent*, don't use a bright colour. (See illustration B on page 142.)

**3.** Next, you'll contour the orbital bone above the crease, using a medium colour or neutral. You can use the same colour you used on your outer lid if it's not too dark, but most women should not wear a light or highly frosted colour on this area because paleness will bring it forward. You need shading to push back the orbital bone, letting your eye shine out. *If you have a small brow area*, you are the exception to the rule and will use a lighter shade on your brow area.

A. First cover your entire eye area with highlighter. If your lid is prominent, cover only the brow area, not the lid.

B. Second, apply a contour shade to the outer third of your lid, almost in the shape of a triangle.

**4.** With your angle brush, again tapping off excess powder before applying, sweep the colour from the *outer* edge of your eye inwards, going all the way across the bone. Start the contour colour just above the crease, blending slightly into the crease to look natural. Be sure you apply the shadow high enough onto the bony area. If it is too low and near the crease, your eyes will look sunken. Be careful, too, not to apply the shadow too low at the outer edge of your eye, or your eye will look droopy. Think of an imaginary line from the outer corner of your eye to the end of your eyebrow, and use this as your boundary.

**For the proportioned eye,** apply your contour shadow just above the crease, from the outer eye to the inner, concentrating most of the colour on the outer two thirds of the orbital bone. As an extra touch, you can then apply an uplifting shade to the inner two thirds of your lid and just under the arch of your brow. If your lid shows a lot, skip this last step.

**If little or no lid shows and you have more brow area,** bring the contour shadow up higher in the centre and extend it a bit closer to the nose, creating almost a semicircular shape. Having shadow higher in the centre will 'open' the eye and prevent a droopy look at the outside edge. You can, if you like, place a dot of uplifter over the centre of your pupil, close to your lashes. Use a colour similar to your eye colour, or pink or silver for brown-eyed Winters and Summers, peach or gold for brown-eyed Autumns and Springs. Don't blend the dot much. The purpose is to make your eye look bigger by extending the 'iris' upwards a bit.

**If little or no lid shows and you have a very small brow area,** apply a pale colour to the entire brow area, from crease to brow, instead of a contour shade. You don't need to push your brow bone back. Choose a colour similar to your eye colour, or use a pink or pale grey for cool seasons, peach or golden yellow for warms. You can then sweep a little of the colour on your outer lid upwards at the corner, towards the end of your eyebrow. Then, if you like, you can place a dot of uplifter on the centre of your lid right over your pupil, close to the lashes. Don't blend it much. This dot will catch the light as your eyes move, and make the iris look bigger.

**If your lid is prominent and you have a small brow area,** you will apply a pale shade across the entire orbital bone, blending it towards the eyebrow. Now brush a little of the darker eye shadow from the outer corner of your lid up towards the end of your eyebrow, feathering it at the outer edge of your orbital bone. Finally, apply a subtle, medium neutral to the inner two thirds of your lid, to recess your lid. (If your crease is dark and sunken, stop the shadow short of the crease. This trick will help make your lid appear smaller, your brow larger.)

**5.** Now blend the shadow with your fluff brush until the edges are soft and the shape on your orbital bone is flattering. For stubborn edges, use your contour brush to blend. Keep your eyes open while looking in the mirror and blending. This way you can adjust the shape and check your boundaries. If, at this point, you feel your eyes need brightening, apply a touch of eye shadow that is similar to the colour of your blusher right on the crest of each orbital bone. Use your fluff brush for subtle application. (You can use blusher as long as you are *sure* the ingredients are safe for the eye area.)

**6.** Next, take your contour brush and lightly blend the entire area, using upward and outward strokes, from lid to brow. Blend until the intensity is just right and the edges are smooth. (If you wear glasses, allow the colour to be more intense.)

**7.** Dust the entire area lightly with translucent powder to set your shadow and help it last all day.

*Proportioned lid and brow*

*Small lid, small brow*

*Small lid, large brow*

*Large lid, small brow*

## STEP 3: MASCARA

For luxurious lashes, apply two coats of mascara to *all* your lashes, top and bottom. A few people will have to skip the bottom, for their lashes grow so close to the skin that their mascara always smears.

**1.** To coat your top lashes, look into the mirror, tip your head back slightly, and stroke on the mascara with your wand. Twirl the wand up and out to cover the lashes completely from the base to the tips.

**2.** To apply mascara to the bottom, tilt your head forward and twirl your wand down and out until the lashes are evenly covered. You may find it easier to use your wand vertically, applying the mascara with the tip of the wand with little downward strokes.

**3.** Comb your lashes with your brow/lash brush to separate them and to remove any clumps of mascara. Allow to dry for a few seconds.

**4.** Dust your lashes lightly with powder to thicken them before you apply your second coat.

**5.** Apply a second coat to top and bottom. (But don't dust with powder this time!)

To correct mistakes, dot the misplaced mascara with a cotton bud dipped in non-oily eye make-up remover.

## *STEP 4: EYEBROWS*

Eyebrows frame your eyes, so you want them to look balanced. If you have kept them well shaped through judicious plucking, you may not have to do anything other than brush them into place with your brow/lash brush. But some of you will need to fill in bare spots or compensate for short or unequal brows, or thinner brows that are extremely sparse. Use the same guidelines for length that you used when you plucked your brows (see page 90). Please use caution. Remember, over-pencilled brows can ruin your looks.

**1.** Take your pencil or brush dipped in pressed powder and feather the colour on with quick, short strokes, to simulate little hairs. Never draw it on – a harsh line will be too obvious and will spoil the natural look you're trying to achieve.

**2.** Finish by brushing your eyebrows up and out with your brow/lash brush. If your brows need a bit of coaxing, use a touch of facial wax on the brush first.

*Voila!* See what a difference eye make-up makes? It takes practice, but it's well worth the trouble. Once you learn the routine, you'll be able to apply your eye make-up in three or four minutes, and with the right colours, you'll have 'naturally' stunning eyes every single day!

# CHAPTER 12

# LIPS

ALTHOUGH we communicate with our eyes, our lips do most of the talking. A woman's smile is the first thing people notice about her face. And surely the most sensual part of a woman's face is her lips. At least they can be, with properly applied lip colour!

Some women are blessed with natural lip colour. Lucky you, if you're one of them. Some of us, however, have almost no rosiness in our lips, and really need that touch of colour to give us a healthy, vibrant glow.

There are three main types of lip products: *lipstick*, *lip gloss*, and *lip pencil*. Lipstick is my favourite because it gives excellent coverage and you have more flexibility and fun with colours. Gloss is sheer, can be tinted or colourless, and adds shine. It can be used to top off lipstick or can be worn alone, if you just want a faint hint of colour. Lip pencils are essential accessories, used to outline your lips and to keep lipstick in place and fresh looking all day.

## CHOOSING THE RIGHT COLOUR

Like blusher, lipstick should complement both your skin tone and your clothing. Again, you can start with one or two basic colours to blend with your wardrobe, and gradually add a collection of shades in your season's palette that will more exactly match the variety of colours in your clothing.

Knowing your season makes it easy to know what colours you want; finding the colours in a shop is harder. You may have to try several brands to find the perfect shades, but shopping and experimenting can be fun, and the right colours will make a world of difference in your appearance.

I strongly suggest that you take a friend shopping with you if you are at all unsure how to judge what's best on you. Remember to periodically update your look. Some women go for years wearing a lipstick that is too light, because that's what they wore at college. Bear in mind, too, that as we age, nature fades our skin tones, hair, and eyes, and a colour that was wonderful in our thirties may become too bright later on.

To shop for lipsticks, start by looking through the tester unit for cool or warm colours, depending on your season. Winters and Summers should scout for *cool pinks and reds*, rather than orange and peach shades. Autumns and Springs should stick to *warm* peach, coral, or peachy pink shades, avoiding hints of blue. To help you choose, compare cool blue-pinks, blue-reds and rose shades with warm yellow-pinks, orange-reds, and peaches. Today, luckily, some companies arrange their testers in warm and cool sections, to make your shopping easier.

After you have identified your range of colours, you need to select the colour value that is best for you. Here's where the Colour Me Beautiful system really works! You'll be amazed at how quickly you can select the perfect colour. First, decide which colour you are choosing – pink *or* plum *or* peach *or* red. In other words, don't try to select all your lipstick colours at the same time. Then, line up the lipsticks you're considering, from light to dark, and try on the shade that seems *medium* bright. If it is perfect, you're in luck. If it's too bright, try on the next lighter shade; if too light, try on the next deeper or brighter shade. Repeat this with each colour you are selecting. You may not find all your colours at the same counter. Remember, if a particular brand doesn't have the right intensity for you, move straight on to the next counter.

Balance the colour of your lipstick with the depth of your colouring. A colour that is perfect for a blonde, fair Autumn will be too pale on a vivid, brunette Autumn. A vivid fuchsia lipstick that flatters a Winter will be overwhelmingly bright on a light-haired Summer, who instead needs a soft fuchsia.

Your lips themselves affect the desired intensity of your lip colour. If your lips are either extra-full or thin, stick with fairly soft colours. Bright shades will accentuate either extreme. If you have vivid natural lip colour, choose a shade that looks fairly soft in the tube. Your lips will intensify the colour and it will look brighter once it's on. Or, choose a sheer formula that is slightly transparent. You may even want to just line your lips with a pencil that matches their natural colour and fill in your lips with gloss.

Here are some guidelines for each season. Again, take your blank Make-up Wardrobe Chart with you so you can fill in the brand and colour of your favourites. If you can't spend the money to buy all the colours you want, you will have the names written down for a future shopping trip.

## Lipstick

● *Winters:* Winters aim for clear, bright shades. Some Winters need softer colours if their lips are quite rosy. If you have lots of lip colour, try a sheer berry colour; for pale lips, try a medium pink or a raspberry. Next, test a slightly frosted pink to see if the vibrancy is better on you. Whichever you choose, your pink, raspberry, or berry lipstick will be your mainstay for every day, and will complement the majority of the colours in your wardrobe.

After you've found the pink you love, look for a luscious red. If your hair is very dark, you can probably wear a true red or blue-red. (Avoid orange-reds; they're not for you!) Lighter Winters might try a softer, geranium colour. If you are afraid of red, find a sheer tint or gloss; it will still be red, but you won't feel like Vampira. You do need *some* red to go with your red clothes.

Next, you will enjoy a fuchsia. There are so many varieties of fuchsia, you'll probably need to try a soft one, a bright one, and a dark one, to see which is the best depth for your colouring. If you don't own any clothing in fuchsia, you could skip this colour, but fuchsia also looks beautiful with your emerald green, royal blue, and purple.

Eventually you'll need a burgundy or plum to go with your burgundy clothing. Most black Winters look gorgeous in burgundy lipstick and can wear it as an everyday colour. If burgundy is too strong for your skin, find a sheer or a lightly frosted shade. Or, try using burgundy pencil to cover your lip completely, and then glaze them with a pale plum or raspberry lipstick. You'll get the colour you need, but softer.

- *Summers:* Start with a soft-to-medium rose or pink. If your lips need colour, go for brighter shades, but if your lips are pink to start with, you may prefer a dusty rose. A delectable pink will be your basic lipstick colour and will go with almost everything in your wardrobe. You will probably want several pinks, ranging from rose pink to some blue-pinks, for variety.

Now you'll want a red to wear with your red clothing. Choose a watermelon shade or a soft blue-red (or both). These may be hard to find. If you can't get the soft red you need, instead choose a cool shade of red that's too bright and tone it down by applying pale pink or a 'white' toner over it. Or, choose a tinted red lip gloss. Avoid all orange reds; they'll clash with your cool skin tone.

Fuchsia is an especially nice choice for your next shade. Many Summers find that fuchsia is one of their best colours because they have so much pink in their skin. Look for a soft or even slightly frosted shade.

Last, choose a soft plum, wine, or mauve shade. Keep the colour fairly light, not heavy. This lipstick will be beautiful with the burgundy, plum, and mauve side of your wardrobe.

- *Autumns:* Choose your colours with special care, as Autumns vary more than any other season. If your hair is light, you will look best in soft, muted shades of tawny peach or cinnamon. You may even find that a brownish honey colour is your best shade for every day. Brown-haired and red-haired Autumns will prefer terracotta tones in more intense shades for their basic, everyday lipstick.

Next, you'll need a lipstick that verges towards pink to wear with the salmon and salmon pinks in your wardrobe. Look for a tawny salmon, which will give you a touch of pink without straying into the cool range. Avoid all blue-pinks and fuchsias; they are much too blue for your warm skin tone.

Now choose a red to go with the red side of your wardrobe. If you look best in muted colours, look for a brick red, one with a slightly brownish tone. If you need brightness, select an orange-red. If you are light-haired and fair, try a sheer formula or a lip gloss.

Next, you'll want an orange or an orange-coral to wear with your brighter outfits. Vividly coloured clothing needs a bright lipstick for balance. Many Autumns will do well with a burnt orange or pumpkin lipstick, but some – redheads, especially – look terrific in true orange (see Sharon, page 34). You might also try creating some beautiful coral shades by combining red with a lighter peach or the 'yellow' lipstick toner most brands carry.

Finally, you may want a mahogany or mocha lipstick to wear with your rich browns or brownish burgundy clothing. Choose a deep shade or a soft muted colour, depending on which intensity is most harmonious on you. Black Autumns look especially terrific in a rich mahogany shade, and may prefer it as their basic, everyday lipstick.

● *Springs:* The most versatile lip colour for a Spring is a clear salmon. Because it is between pink and peach, it blends well with all your wardrobe colours and is a great basic. Some blonde Springs, however, love a pink lipstick and will prefer it as their everyday colour. Other Springs, the redheads, often prefer peach as their basic. Whichever you choose to start with – salmon, warm pink, or peach – look for light-to-medium, clear colours, and avoid all muted, brownish shades. Also avoid blue-pinks or fuchsias, as they are much too cool for you.

If you chose peach as your everyday basic, you'll now need a warm pink or coral pink to wear with your pink clothing. By the same token, if pink is your basic, select a peach or apricot to go with the peach side of your wardrobe. And then add the salmon. You will love having all three of these colours to enjoy with your Spring clothing.

Next, look for a coral in a slightly bright shade to wear with your brighter clothing.

Finally, look for a red. Some Springs, especially brunettes and red-heads, wear a clear orange-red beautifully. If you want it a bit less bright, try toning it down by applying pale peach on top. Softer Springs need a lightly frosted poppy shade. If you are afraid of red, you can try a sheer red lip gloss; but most Springs look perkier with a touch of real colour, rather than gloss, on their lips.

## Lip Pencil

Make your next purchase a lip pencil, even if you've never tried one. Lip pencils are invaluable, both for giving lips definition and for keeping lipstick from 'bleeding' at the edges. They can also be used to cover the lips entirely as a base for lipstick or lip gloss. With a lip pencil foundation, colour will stay on all day.

Choose a lip pencil that matches your lipstick colour closely so your outlining won't show. If you want to minimise your lips, use a pencil that is slightly deeper than your lipstick. To make your lips look fuller, use a pencil that is lighter than your lipstick. You can also soften the look of a bright lipstick with an outline of lighter pencil; or, if you want a softer lip colour, but don't want to look faded, line with a deeper pencil and fill in with the soft colour. Always be sure to blend the lipstick over the liner to completely to obscure your out-lining. A sharp line looks unnatural and harsh.

You can create 'new' shades be covering your lips with pencil and adding various shades of lipstick on top. For example, you might cover your lips with your season's red liner and then apply a cool pink or a warm peach lipstick over it to create an exciting blend. Try it! It's fun to play with your colours.

## Lipstick Toners

You might also want to purchase a lipstick toner – yellow gold for Autumns and Springs, silvery white for Summers and Winters. These gleamers are usually slightly frosted and are terrific for toning down bright colours or for creating shimmering new shades. They can also be used right in the centre of your lower lip, on top of your lipstick, to give you a 'pout'.

## *CHOOSING THE RIGHT FORMULA*

**Lipsticks** come in cream and frosted formulas, usually in tubes, but sometimes in little pans that require a brush for application. Cream lipsticks range from those with lots of pigment, hence thicker cover-age and stronger colour, to sheer colours that, while not transparent, give a lighter, softer effect. Generally, the thicker creams stay on better because of the extra pigment and thicker wax. The sheers have a moist, shiny look, due to their higher oil content, but they do not stay on long. Some women prefer them for their lighter feeling on the lips as well as their softer colour – but you do have to reapply them more often.

Frosted lipsticks have a pearlised, sparkly look and usually provide opaque, rather than sheer, coverage. The pearl content ranges from minimal to extreme. Most women can wear a slightly frosted shade, especially at night, but few except the very young will be flattered by a highly frosted lip colour. Frosted lipsticks stay on well, because they are a bit drier, and the colour usually doesn't change on your lips after you've worn it a while, the way some creams do.

**Lip gloss** is sheer and transparent, and comes in a tube, a wand, or a pot. It doesn't stay on long, but gives a subtle, natural hint of colour and keeps the lip moist.

**Lip pencils** are made with much harder wax and less oil than lipstick. Consequently they stay on well, but they can dry your lips if you use them to cover your entire lip area.

If your lips are pale, you will probably prefer the more opaque lipsticks that cover well – the creams or frosts – for their greater colour impact. If you have lips that are naturally rosy, or if you prefer subtle lip colour, you'll like the sheer lipstick formulas or lip glosses best. Try different formulas to find your favourite. Some companies offer their colours in several formulas to give you a choice.

Lipsticks tend to have three potential problems: 'bleeding', breaking, and drying the lips.

• Lipsticks bleed for two reasons – the formula or your lips. The sheer, moist, formulas (especially in red or darker colours) tend to run more easily, especially in hot weather or on a woman with oily skin. If your lips do not have distinct ridges as boundaries, or have feathery lines around the edges, you will have more trouble with lipsticks 'bleeding'. To correct the problem, choose a harder cream formula, one that pulls a bit as you apply it, or a frost. Or avoid moisturiser around the edge of your mouth, use a lip pencil to outline your lips, and powder your lips before applying the colour.

• Lipsticks that consistently break usually have a formula that is too soft. If you love the colour, but it gets too squishy every time you buy it, write the manufacturer and tell him. He can adjust the formula, and probably will if he gets enough complaints. Don't leave your lipsticks in a hot car during the summertime. Wax is wax, and it can only take so much heat without melting.

• Lipsticks that are drying or make your lips peel usually have formulas that contain a lot a talc or other fillers to compensate for a lack of pigment. Try changing brands, and avoid frosts, since they tend to be a bit drying. In the wintertime, your lips may dry out no matter what lipstick you use, especially if you have dry skin. Try treating your lips at night with vitamin E, or applying an aloe vera cream before you put on your lipstick. (Vitamin E is too greasy to wear under your lipstick. The colour will slide right off.)

Now you can see why cosmetics companies guard their formulas so carefully. All women want a lipstick that is moist and creamy but also stays on and doesn't bleed. Contradictory traits! To make a lipstick stay on, it must be made from a harder wax, with less oil, and will necessarily be a bit drier and less shiny. And to have the moist, creamy look, a lipstick will have to sacrifice its staying power. Ah, for the perfect mixture!

## *INGREDIENTS AND SENSITIVITIES*

In addition to oil, wax, and pigments, lipsticks contain fillers, binders, preservatives, and (usually) fragrance to mask their musky smell. Frosted lipsticks also contain mica.

All lip products are not created equal. Some formulas contain extra, protective ingredients, such as PABA (sunscreen), or vitamins A and E (conditioners and emollients).

Additives that can prompt reactions include lanolin, PABA (even though it's good, some people are allergic to it), and colouring agents. If you're having trouble, change to a different colour, a different brand, or try a hypoallergenic formula.

## *APPLYING LIP COLOUR*

The first key to beautiful lips is definition. Some women have lips with a natural outline around the edges. Most of us, however, have lips that blend into our faces and really need to be outlined with a lip pencil or a lip brush. Whether the colour is soft and subtle or bold and dramatic, it's definition that gives us that elegant, finished look.

It is imperative that you apply your lipstick straight and evenly, especially at the corners of your mouth – another convincing reason to use a lip pencil or a brush to outline your lips! Nothing looks worse than a messy swipe of colour that leaves your lips crooked and unbalanced.

Your goal is luscious lips with a natural line and shape. If you feel your lips are too full or too thin, or if the corners turn down, I've included some special tips at the end of this section. Here are the easy steps for applying your lipstick perfectly every time. Use the same principles for lip gloss.

**1.** With a lip pencil or a lipstick brush turned sideways to make a thin line, draw along your upper lip line from the outer left corner to the centre, and then from the outer right corner to the centre. If you are more comfortable working from the centre to the corners, that's fine, too. But never draw one continuous line from left to right, or your lips will be crooked. Follow your natural lip line and don't make the bow of your lip too pointed. The peak of the bow is usually under your nostrils.

**2.** Next, draw your lower lip line, again from each corner into the centre.

**3.** Now, fill in with your lipstick or gloss. You can apply either straight from the tube, bringing the colour right up to your liner, or you can dab it on with a brush. A brush is handy because it lets you control the coverage, making it as thick or thin as you like. If you've used a lip liner in a different shade from your lipstick, blend it well so its edges don't show.

**4.** Check to see if your lips look straight. If you've gone over or under the boundaries here and there, simply touch up and straighten with your lip pencil or brush.

**5.** To make your lipstick stay on longer, blot your lips, powder them, and then reapply the colour. The talc from the powder will help your lipstick cling. Apply gloss on top if you want a shiny finish. (Do not powder your lips if you are applying lip gloss by itself.)

**6.** Look at your total face in the mirror and see if the colours are in balance – cheeks, eyes, lips. Perhaps now that you've added lipstick you need a bit more blusher. If not, your make-up is finished!

## SPECIAL TIPS

**If your lips are full,** try applying your lip pencil just *inside* your natural lip line. Remember, you can also use a lip pencil darker than your lipstick to help the narrowing effect.

**If your lips are thin,** extend your lip pencil just *outside* your natural lip line. A pencil lighter than your lipstick will give your lips a little extra fullness, too.

**If your lips are unbalanced,** apply the liner just *outside* your natural lip line on the thin lip, just *inside* on the full lip. Refer to the contouring section in Chapter 8 or more tips on balancing lips.

**If your lips go downwards on the ends,** you can give yourself a 'lift' by slightly raising the corners of your lips. Here's how. Either pencil in the corners of your upper lip to turn upward, or stop the corner short on the upper lip so the lower lip extends at the corners. Either technique will give the illusion of lips that 'smile' at the corners. Don't overdo.

Don't carry any of these strategies too far or your lips will end up looking comical. If people can see that your lips are drawn on, the distraction will counteract any benefits you were hoping for.

Now practise! The effort will quickly pay off. Soon applying lipstick will be second nature, and you'll be able to do it perfectly in one minute or less – small effort for such glamorous results!

Now, with your make-up done, how do you feel? I hope the answer is 'Fabulous!' You deserve that wonderful feeling – to hold your head a little higher, to stand a little taller, to straighten your shoulders – just to bask in a warm glow of confidence. Why not feel proud of the way you look, worthy of being noticed and happy to show off the beautiful creation that you are?

# EVENING

EVENING is your chance to sparkle and to add a little drama to your make-up. Low, flattering lights allow you to deepen or brighten your colours without appearing overdone. Shimmering, frosted shades inappropriate for day wear look subtle and beautiful by candleglow. At night you can let your imagination run to more glamorous effects.

As always, your season will guide you in choosing your colour for nighttime dazzle.

## STEPS FOR A BEAUTIFUL EVENING

When the evening is special, allow extra time to take a relaxing bath and to apply your make-up carefully. Plan ahead so you can treat your face to a scrub and mask that will leave it tingling and radiantly clean. After toning as usual, begin your make-up magic:

**1.** Apply your foundation (a *little* heavier, if you wish) to cover any flaws.

**2.** Next, cover any circles under your eyes, lines around mouth and nose with concealer. Pat to blend. (At night you may prefer to apply concealer first, under your foundation, for extra coverage.)

**3.** Contour the hollows under your cheeks by patting on a darker foundation with your contour sponge, or brush on pressed powder in a darker shade, blending the edges. Give your nostrils a bit of flare by brushing darker foundation in the bevels at either side of the tip of your nose. You might want to follow some of the tips in Chapter 8 to sculpt other areas of your face.

**4.** Now powder your entire face. Dip your powder brush first in your blusher, then in your powder, and add a subtle glow of radiance to your whole face.

**5.** Apply blusher as usual. With your fan brush, sweep a brighter shade, for extra glow, right on the crest of your cheekbone.

**6.** You can line your eyes a little more dramatically than usual. Now's your chance to use black (if your lashes are dark) or a colour such as blue, green, or violet to enhance the colour of your eyes. Or, use a neutral on the bottom and a colour on your upper lashes. (Again, balance the colour with your colouring. A woman with blonde hair and lashes does not look attractive with heavy black eyeliner, even at night.)

**7.** Apply your eye shadow as usual, but now you can use frosted shades. Also, try using a deeper colour than your daytime shadow, or simply top off your regular shade with a deeper or brighter shade just on the outer corner of your lid. Start with your highlighter and cover the eye area. Add your glamorous colour to the outer third of your lid, blending it up onto the outer third of your eyebrow only as far as the end of your brow. Now apply a medium to dark shade across the rest of your orbital bone. This contour shade should not be frosted, especially if your bone protrudes.

**8.** Now for a note of sparkle. Apply a pale frosted or iridescent 'stripe' of shadow to the centre of your eyelid, placing it directly over your pupil. Try silver or pearly pink for the cool seasons, gold or frosty peach for the warms. (If your eyelids show a lot, use a medium neutral shade in a minimum frost instead.) The shimmery shadow will catch the light as you move your eyes, making them magnetising. Blend the gleaming shadow into the edges of the darker shade.

If you have room on your upper brow bone, apply another dot of frost just under the arch, blending it well, to lift the eye.

Add a third glimmer at the outer edge of the eye, right in the crease, just under your darker shadow, to lift your eye. Blend the dot upwards to dispel any droopiness.

**9.** If your eyes are not sensitive, line the rim of your lower lid inside your lashes with a kohl pencil in the same colour as your liner. (Be sure to use a pencil that is safe for use near the eye.) Lining the inner rim will make your eyes look slightly smaller, but they will look more dramatic. If your eyes are very small, try lining the inner rim with a white pencil instead, which will make the whites of your eyes look bigger. If you don't feel comfortable putting make-up on your inside rims, feel free to skip this step.

**10.** Next, apply your mascara – the first coat. Separate your lashes with your brow/lash brush and let the mascara dry.

**11.** Powder your entire face again, including the eye area, with loose, translucent powder, using downward strokes. You are looking smooth and flawless by now.

**12.** Now dust on some more sparkle: Use your fan brush to apply loose iridescent powder – silver for the cool seasons, gold for the warms – and sweep it across your cheekbones, the tips of your nose and chin, and over your upper forehead. With a clean eye sponge, apply the iridescent powder more heavily along the top of your cheekbone (but not into the circular area under your eye).

If you prefer, you can lightly dust your entire face with iridescent powder. And if you are bare-shouldered, shimmer it across your shoulders and your collarbone, too.

**13.** Apply your second coat of mascara and separate your lashes with your brow/lash brush. By now they should look full and luxuriant.

**14.** Finally, it's time for lipstick. You can use deeper or brighter shades than your daytime colour, balancing them with the colour of your clothing. For example, Winter's black dress calls for red or deep pink lips; while a Spring's pastel ensemble calls for medium to pastel lip colour. In the centre of your lower lip apply a dab of frosted silver or golden lip gleamer to give yourself a charming pout. For a gleaming, moist finish, cover your lips with clear gloss.

**15.** Cheek yourself in the mirror to see that the colours of eyes, cheeks, and lips are in balance. Use powder to tone down an area; add more colour to brighten. Perfect.

Feeling glamorous? You are!

# Part III

# FINISHING TOUCHES

# NAILS

ANY of us let our fingers do the walking and our hands do the talking, yet don't even consider them in our beauty rituals. Next to your face, there is no other part of your body that is so much in the public eye. I have seen women who, at first glance, look impeccably groomed, only to notice later that their nails are chipped and their hands look rough.

None of us wants unattractive hands, but most of us do not want to spend a lot of money on a professional manicure. With a few supplies, some simple guidelines, and less than an hour of time, you can do a perfect manicure at home that will last for a week at least. Isn't that worth it?

## CHOOSING THE RIGHT COLOURS

Your nail colour should match or blend with your lip colour, so you can use the lipstick colours from your season's palette as a shopping guide for purchasing nail colours as well. If you plan to wear a variety of colours during the course of any given week, you will need to wear a versatile shade of nail polish – one that will blend with most of your lipsticks and the colours in your wardrobe – and save those bright reds, fuchsias, or corals for special occasions. (Or plan your wardrobe a week at a time so you are wearing all colours that will go with, say, red lipstick and nail varnish.) If your nails are short, they will look better in softer, neutral colours rather than dark or bright ones.

Safe shades for each season are:

• *Winter:* a medium rose or strawberry shade, one that blends with both reds and pinks.

• *Summer:* a soft rose or soft strawberry, again to bridge the spectrum between red and pinks.

• *Autumn:* a mocha or tawny peach, fairly muted, so it will go with your soft colours as well as your reds.

• *Spring:* a soft salmon, not too pink, not too orange, to cover the span of your wardrobe.

To ensure that your nail varnish stays fresh and applies smoothly, you want to take a few precautions. First, keep your bottles of nail colour away from heat because heat will thicken the varnish – plus, it's highly flammable. You can keep it fresh the longest if you store it in the refrigerator!

Nail colour will 'bubble' if it is applied too thickly and not allowed to dry between coats, if it is applied in the wind or sun or too close to a heat source, or if it is too old or thick. If you have a bottle of favourite nail colour that has thickened, you can buy varnish thinner. Don't try to thin your varnish with varnish remover. The ingredients are totally different, and it won't work.

## NAIL-CARE PRODUCTS

To give yourself a manicure that lasts, you'll need to assemble the proper tools and products. If you don't already own them, you'll find these items available in most chemists. You'll see when to use each as we go through the steps for a perfect manicure.

### Varnish Remover

Varnish remover comes in bottles for use with cottonwool balls, or in sponge-filled jars into which you dip your fingers and rub the nail against the sponge. I recommend acetone-free formulas, as they are less drying to your nails and cuticles.

### Cottonwool Balls or Pads

Cottonwool balls come in two sizes. The larger ones are more practical for polish removal. Pads are ideal.

### Emery Board or Diamond File

Your emery board or nail file is used to shape your nails and maintain their desired length. The emery has a rough and a smooth side, is made of woody fibres and will wear out with use. The metal diamond file lasts longer, but doesn't file your nails as smoothly.

### Liquid Cuticle Remover

Cuticle remover is used to soften your cuticles and help 'float' off the dead skin.

### Cuticle (Orange) Stick

A cuticle stick is pointed at one end and flat at the other. Originally made from orange wood, these are used to push back the cuticle and will not damage the matrix, which is the part from which the nail grows. A damaged matrix can cause the nail to grow out lumpy and irregular.

### Base and Top Coats

Base and top coats are both important and each has a specific use. The base coat holds the colour on the nail and the top coat seals it from damage and makes it last longer.

### Nail Varnish

Varnish comes in cream and frost formulas. Either is fine, though cream is more appropriate for the office. A good brand should stay on for five to seven days, depending on what you do with your hands. Obviously, scouring pots and pans will shorten the life of your manicure, no matter how good the varnish.

### Rich Hand Cream

Use a hand cream or body lotion that's extra rich and special for your manicure. You can even use your favourite moisturising cream.

### Cuticle Cream

Cuticle cream is thicker than hand cream. If you rub it on your cuticles every night, it will help preserve your manicure and keep your cuticles smooth and lovely.

## Cuticle Clippers

Cuticle clippers are used to clip hangnails or jagged bits of cuticles. They come in both scissor-type handles or palm-grips. Use whichever is more comfortable for you, but shop for as good a pair as you can afford. Used as described below, they prevent many a painful nail disaster.

## *STEPS TO A PERFECT MANICURE*

Now it's time to hide the phone, turn on some music, and make those fingers match the rest of your Colour Me Beautiful image!

**1.** Assemble the tools listed above and, in addition, gather the following items.
• Bowl of warm, soapy water
• Bowl of warm, clear water
• Two hand towels
Place one hand towel out flat on your table and arrange the other supplies on top.

**2.** Remove your old nail colour. Dampen a cottonwool ball with varnish remover and remove every last trace of old colour. Don't forget the area closest to your cuticles. Even if you aren't wearing nail colour, it's a good idea to do this step anyway to remove any traces of oil or cream.

**3.** Shape your nails with your emery board or nail file. It is important to shape them when they are dry because wet nails are weaker and can be easily damaged. File them from the outside edge in to the centre, avoiding a back-and-forth sawing motion, because this can weaken your nails. Be careful not to file into the cuticles at the corners. Your nail shape should follow the contour of the ends of your fingers rather than be too pointed or squared.

**4.** Soak your nails in the warm, soapy water for three minutes to soften the cuticles and loosen dirt that may have become embedded beneath the tips of your nails. Use the pointed end of your cuticle stick to remove dirt. Then blot your hands on your towel.

**5.** Now apply your cuticle remover according to the directions on the bottle and allow it to remain on for three to five minutes. Using the wedge-shaped end of your cuticle stick, gently push back your cuticles. Then swish your nails in the sudsy water and massage them to remove any residue. Rinse your nails in the warm, clear water, and

*File your nails so the shape follows the contour of your fingertips – oval rather than pointed or square.*

then dry them well, gently using the towel to finish pushing back the cuticles.

**6.** Before you continue, wrap or 'twist' a small amount of cottonwool around the end of your cuticle stick. You may need to use this later dipped in varnish remover to 'erase' any nail colour that gets onto your cuticles. (Cotton buds are too fuzzy for this purpose.)

**7.** If you have any hangnails or a cuticle that is jagged, clip the snag ONLY. Do not cut your cuticles otherwise, or they will become rough and jagged all the time.

**8.** Apply base coat. This step is important in assuring that your varnish will adhere better, go on smoother, and not stain your nails. This one step can make the difference in how long your manicure will last! The base coat will remain slightly sticky, and will have a dull finish. Apply base coat from the base of your nail to the tip using three strokes – one in the centre and one on each side. Using a lot of little strokes or reapplying in areas already covered will cause a 'lumpy' application and will delay drying time. Allow the base coat to dry for one minute. If your nails have ridges, apply a second coat.

**9.** Now apply varnish using the same three-stroke method. Allow the first coat to dry for three minutes, and then apply a second coat and allow it to dry for five minutes. If any varnish gets on your cuticles, now is the time to carefully use your cuticle stick moistened with varnish remover to 'erase' your mistakes.

**10.** Apply top coat in the same three-stroke method, 'wrapping' it over the tip of your nail to protect the edge of the nail colour. Allow your top coat to dry for at least fifteen minutes. This is one case when more is better, so a half hour or more is terrific, if you can spare the time! (You can try one of the new 'quick-dry' products to speed up the drying process.) To ensure that your manicure lasts as long as possible, repeat this step every day. (It will only take the top coat five minutes to dry on a daily basis.)

**11.** When your nails are thoroughly dry, massage a rich hand cream into your hands. The backs of hands have no oil glands so concentrate cream there and around your cuticles.

On a nightly basis, apply cuticle cream to each nail. Keep the cream by your bedside so you'll get in the habit of using it. It only takes a few seconds and your cuticles will stay smooth and lovely, which not only looks and feels better, but also lessens the amount of time it takes to do your next manicure!

## *SPECIAL PROBLEMS*

Some of us are born lucky, with nails that grow like weeds and never seem to break. Others have nails that break or split easily and are harder to manage. All of us, from time to time, may have special problems in keeping our nails attractive. Here are the most common problems and their solutions.

**Yellowing Nails:** Chemicals used in film processing, topically applied medications, nicotine, and darker nail colour dyes can turn nails yellow. Always use gloves when working with chemicals, wash hands well after applying medications, and use a base coat before applying nail polish. You can remove some of the yellow staining by soaking your nails for a few minutes in lemon juice.

**Breaking, Peeling, Splitting Nails:** These problems can be caused by heredity and also by damage to the cuticle or matrix. Be especially careful not to damage your matrix with the nail clippers when snipping problem spots. Also, overfiling your nails at the corners can cause weakness, so you will need to file your nails slightly more squarish to give the sides added strength. Constant exposure to water, as well as dryness from climate, detergents, or chemicals can cause nails to be brittle. It pays to use gloves when doing harsh chores and to use a good hand cream to moisturise your hands and nails. If they are already abused, try an extra-rich cuticle cream at night or rub a coat of baby oil or petroleum jelly over your hands and cuticles, slip on cotton cosmetic gloves (found in chemists), and sleep with them on. The warmth of your body combined with the oils will help soften and lubricate your skin, cuticles, and nails.

In addition, you may want to try the special varnishes called 'nail hardener', made specifically for problem nails. They are usually sold with special base and top coats as well, and they do seem to help.

And try to remember not to use your nails as screwdrivers, lid openers, or pot scrubbers!

**Ridges and 'Funny' Colourations:** Horizontal ridges may reflect a past illness, especially one with a fever, or damage to the matrix, and will eventually grow out. Vertical ridges are genetic and also tend to occur as we age. Gentle polishing, a liquid ridge filler, and/or two coats of base coat can all help smooth out the surface of your nail.

Variations in colour can indicate a health problem. If you are light-skinned, your bare nails should match the back of your hand; if dark-skinned, the palm. Anaemia can turn nails white; heart or lung problems can make them look blue. Are your nails half-white, half-pink? This could indicate a kidney ailment. If you notice any unexplained change in your nails, see a doctor for answers.

**Nail Biting:** This is a hard habit to break since often you are not even aware you are doing it. It really helps to keep your nails and cuticles smooth from any tempting snags or rough edges. I have a friend with a nail-biting teenage daughter who treated her to weekly manicures until her nails had grown out. It worked! Not only did the manicures keep the area smooth, but a further incentive was the immediate gratification of seeing her hands look better.

Applying false nails can also give your nails protection from your teeth, and an immediate improvement in their looks, but there is one caution. As the false nails begin to fall off, they can take a layer of natural nail off with them, leaving your nail weaker than ever. If you decide to wear false nails, be sure you buy the appropriate nail remover to dissolve the glue – and not your nail – when you want to remove them.

It's a great idea if you can set aside a weekly time to manicure your nails, maybe while you watch your favourite TV programme. With your cuticles kept in good condition, a manicure will take only half an hour. I know I always feel extra good about myself when my nails and hands look their best.

# HAIR

WHENEVER I teach a make-up class, invariably I am asked, 'What shall I do with my hair?' It's a great question. Most of us don't feel good about ourselves if we don't feel good about our hair. Even with make-up on, we cannot achieve an image we want if we feel our hair is not right.

Hair requires two considerations: colour and style. Both are important, but for different reasons. Colour should flatter and harmonise with our skin and eyes. Style creates balance and line.

## COLOUR

Nature gives us the hair that goes with our colouring. For many of us, the colour we have now is the best. However, many women want to cover grey, stay blonde, or simply enhance their natural hair colour.

To enhance your hair colour, you must choose a colour that complements your skin tone. Your natural hair colour is your best guideline. Totally changing your hair will detract from the beauty of your skin tone. The wrong hair colour will clash just as badly as wearing the wrong make-up colours. Your skin may look muddy, sallow, or even dirty.

Maintaining the blonde hair you had as a child or covering grey hair is easy if you use your season and your original hair colour as a guideline.

Hair colouring products abound, ranging from colour that can be washed out to dyes that change the hair permanently until new hair grows in. Here are the most common types.

### Temporary colour

Mousses and shampoos have no peroxide, ammonia, or any other chemicals to penetrate the hair's outer layer. They consist of pigment (mixed with water) that stays on the hair surface. They are designed only for subtle changes and for short-term use. They will wash out – or even brush out – quickly. Never use these products immediately after a perm or other chemical process because the hair has then been made porous and will take the colour with unnatural intensity.

### Semi-permanent colour

These have little or no peroxide and simply coat the outer shaft of the hair, primarily with a waxy lotion and pigment. They gradually wear off each time you shampoo. The advantage is that they do not strip the hair and expose red or yellow pigment – especially important for the cool seasons, Winters and Summers, who do not want red tones. The disadvantage is that they do not last as long as permanent colour.

### Permanent colour

These products contain peroxide or other chemicals that penetrate the hair shaft and actually change the hair's natural colour. The chemical strips the colour from dark to light. Depending on the length of time the product is left on, the hair goes through the following changes in colour, starting from black or brown: dark red, orange-red, orange, coin gold, yellow gold, yellow, pale yellow, white.

After the peroxide or stripping agent works, the pigment then penetrates the hair with a new colour. Often this is a one-step process, with both the chemical lightener and the pigment deposits doing their jobs at the same time.

**Lowlighting** however, is a two-step process. First it's necessary to strip the hair of its natural colour, to the pale yellow stage. Then the desired shade of blonde is applied.

**Streaking and highlighting** are one-step processes. The hair is simply stripped to the desired level of natural pigment and left at that.

Some of the permanent products have more peroxide and less pigment, while other brands have more pigment, less peroxide. The brands with more peroxide tend to bring out more red and are best for Autumns and Springs or blonde Summers. Cool seasons are best with the low peroxide/high pigment brands.

The advantage of permanent hair colour is its longevity. However, in a few weeks the hair oxidises, and gradually the stripped, reddish hair shows through, a problem for the cool seasons who want to avoid red or gold tones.

With this information, and knowledge of your desired goal, you and your hairdresser should be able to achieve the look you want. On the following pages you'll learn the perfect hair colours for your season. Whether you want to cover grey, stay blonde, or simply enhance your natural colour, using the right colour is the secret to successful results. I have often seen just the tiniest change in hair colour improve a woman's looks dramatically!

## WINTER

A Winter usually has brown or black hair. She looks wonderful with her dark hair because it provides the contrast that is so becoming to her. She would do best to leave her hair as it is. She should never dye her hair blonde or red, as these golden tones are unflattering to her skin and her wardrobe. Occasionally, a Winter is born with platinum blonde hair that remains blonde. It's a striking look, and she needn't alter it. Achieving platinum hair with the bottle is less desirable because it looks artificial and the dark roots show so quickly.

If a Winter craves red hair, she can use an aubergine- or violet-based rinse rather than an orange-red tone. The purplish cast, if subtle, will blend with her complexion. Often a Winter can slightly darken her hair to add further contrast and drama. Be careful not to overdo, or the look will be harsh. A vegetable product, such as henna, in a clear or black or aubergine shade can be attractive; it adds shine and depth but maintains the cool highlights she needs.

If your hair turns orange from a perm, you may need to colour it brown again to maintain a cooler shade. If your hair is not damaged, use a semi-permanent product or a low peroxide permanent one.

Winters should avoid lowlighting or highlighting. Lowlighting will dull their looks, making them look grey and older. The peroxide used for highlighting or lowlighting will bring out orange or gold, unharmonious with Winter skin. A black-haired Winter can create a thick, dramatic streak through her fringe by stripping the hair all the way to white. If you can only succeed in achieving blonde rather than white, forget it. It won't look good.

To cover grey, a Winter should again avoid red tones. Always look for products that say 'ash' rather than 'warm'. To cover a small amount of grey, use the semi-permanent products with no peroxide. Choose a shade *lighter* than your existing brown hair; otherwise, your brown hair will get darker too, and the overall effect will be too dark. Once your hair is mostly grey, you can use a permanent product, preferably a brand with a high-pigment content. Choose a colour as close as possible to your original colour. If your hair was black, you will need to settle for dark brown; solid black dye looks harsh on anyone. It's a good idea to leave a little grey showing for softness. The hairdresser can wrap some strands of your grey hair in foil and keep it from being coloured.

A Winter will often grey in a silvery tone, a salt-and-pepper look, or pure white. The effect can be so beautiful that you may want to leave it natural.

## SUMMER

Summer women, like Winters, want to maintain an ashy tone to their hair and avoid red tones. Even though a few Summer brunettes have red highlights, these highlights will by nature be purplish rather than orange. Like Winter, a Summer brunette would do best to leave her hair natural. The beautiful ashy tone (which she often calls 'mousey') looks gorgeous when she wears her palette of cool colours in make-up and wardrobe. If she insists on red tones in her hair, she should use only a subtle aubergine shade, avoiding any hint of orange.

Most Summer women who were blondes through their teens want to stay blonde. Blonde hair will look great because these Summers have a blonde complexion and don't need dark hair for contrast. Be sure to choose an ash or pale beige blonde tone but do not overdo and turn your hair ashy green. You can still be a yellow blonde; just avoid the yellow that is brassy or golden. If your hair is light brown, you may want to frost your hair to achieve a blonde effect. Have your hairdresser strip your hair to the pale yellow stage, and then apply a soft beige, champagne, or ash blonde to the frosted strands.

Be careful not to become so blonde that you lose all the contrast your hair gave you, thus making your face pale. If you are naturally a light blonde, nature will have made your complexion to go with it. But if you are light brunette, your skin needs some contrast, so choose a dark blonde shade or leave some brown mixed with the blonde to add depth.

Summer women usually grey to a dusty silver, blue grey, or a pearly white shade. A Summer brunette who is greying can simply return her hair to its original brown or a shade slightly lighter. To cover small amounts of grey, use a semi-permanent product in a light brown shade. If your hair is mostly grey, you can use a permanent product to obtain a truer and more lasting colour. Like Winter, avoid reddish or warm shades. Look for colours labelled 'ash', 'beige', 'champagne', or 'cool'. Avoid 'flaxen', 'honey', 'golden', 'red', or 'warm'.

If you were a blonde, you can strip the grey to a pale yellow and apply blonde toner. Or try the reverse: colour some of the grey hair a light brown, leaving the rest. If your hair has turned a pearl white, either leave it as it or cover with a champagne or ash blonde toner.

Some Summers grey in a salt-and-pepper fashion, similar to Winters. If you are so lucky, you may want to leave it natural. Nature has given you that expensive frosted look so many women strive to achieve. Other Summers, once completely grey, have a subtle bluish cast to their hair. It, too, is beautiful as it is.

# AUTUMN

Autumn women are lucky. Because they look great in warm hair colours, they can have fun colouring their hair. Most Autumns, whether blondes, brunettes, or redheads, have either red, copper, or gold highlights in their natural hair colour. Because hair colouring products tend to bring out red or gold in the hair shaft, the Autumn doesn't have to worry. Choose products that say 'warm', 'honey', 'gold', 'red', or 'copper'. Avoid ash or cool shades.

Brunette Autumns can either leave their hair its natural colour or use vegetable dyes or rinses to bring out red highlights. You can usually even become a full-fledged redhead if you want to. I know of several Autumns with almost black hair who, after they went grey, coloured their hair red. It looked even better than their original dark colour!

Auburn and redheaded Autumns can deepen their hair colour if they want to enhance the red tones, or they can use streaking to bring out red or golden highlights. Some colouring techniques create several layers of different colours, which can be beautiful on these warm-season beauties. Your hairdresser can strip the sections of hair to various stages of copper, red, orange, and gold.

Light golden brown or blonde-haired Autumns should choose golden colours. Streaking is great because it leaves some of the dark blonde or light golden brown hair for depth and contrast. Streaking is better than lowlighting on Autumns because it's bolder, with a broader modulation, rather than the overall two-tone effect. Blonde Autumns need richness to avoid looking pale. Have your hairdresser strip your hair to the yellow or coin gold stage, but not lighter. You want a metallic, golden look.

Autumns' grey is slightly yellowish or an oyster white. If you are a blonde, your grey will look blonde too, and you really don't need to cover it. If it looks truly grey, and you feel older or simply don't like it, then return it to a golden blonde.

Redheaded and brunette Autumns, in the greying stages, usually look better when they cover the grey. It's easy to cover your grey because you can wear all the warm hair tones so well. Choose a colour just a shade lighter than your original colour of red or brown. You can leave a grey shock or two in the fringe and at the temples to give an elegant, sophisticated look and keep the frame of your face a bit softer. Once your hair becomes heavily grey, it can be a beautiful, muted, dusty shade, most attractive with all the warm colours in your palette.

If your hair has turned oyster, it can look wonderfully dramatic. Unless it makes you feel older, leave it. If you want to colour it, you may need to go for a light brown rather than blonde. The blonde may look too soft and Springlike, and you'll lose the impact you had with white. You will have to experiment with shades.

## SPRING

Spring, like Autumn, looks terrific in warm hair tones and can easily colour her hair with success. She does not, however, want the metallic look of Autumn. What looks rich on an Autumn will look brassy on a Spring. Spring instead strives for soft, warm tones.

Brunette and redheaded Springs look terrific as they are. You can lighten your hair a bit, if you like. Avoid getting too coppery or you will look like an Autumn. Your skin demands delicacy, even if your hair is dark. Vegetable dyes or rinses are good because they just add sheen and a hint of colour. Highlighting to lift the colour here and there is fine also. A Spring does not want to darken her hair because then she risks looking harsh.

Many Springs were blondes in childhood. A few even stay flaxen blonde throughout their lives. Most, however, begin to darken during during their teens. If your face needs contrast, it's best to leave your hair darkish and add streaks for the blonde effect you like. If you still have a blonde complexion, you can certainly go ahead and be blonde.

To achieve Spring blonde, your hairdresser should strip your hair past the coin gold stage to yellow or pale yellow. You can apply colours ranging from beige to clear, light yellow blonde. An overall blonding looks great on Spring, because she looks good in brightness and clarity. Thick streaks of pale blonde 'sunlight' will also work well, especially if her roots are brown and she doesn't want the hassle of colouring her hair every week or two. Lowlighting is too muted a look for Spring.

Spring's grey has an ivory cast or even a reddish tinge. Many light-haired Springs actually look blonde as they grey because the grey is so yellow. If you are lucky enough to have 'blonde' grey or to have a head of solid ivory white hair, leave it as it is if you're comfortable with it. If you are a dark brunette Spring or a deep redhead, you are better to cover the grey. The two-tone look is not flattering. Once completely grey, your brightness returns.

To cover grey, colour it a soft golden blonde, red, or light brown, depending on your original hair colour. If you are covering only a small percentage of grey, choose a shade lighter than your original colour. You don't want the nongrey hair to become too dark. Once you are mostly grey, choose a shade closer to your original colour, or lighter, as you prefer. Often, brunette Springs look great as blondes once their hair greys.


## ALL SEASONS

When colouring your hair, always consider the amount of contrast you need next to your face. Don't make yourself look pale with hair that's too light, or harsh with hair too dark. Soften the shade with age, but dark-haired Winters and Autumns should never go too light – just a shade or two lighter than your pre-grey hair colour. You need contrast. All grey hair must be kept relatively short, with a meticulous, stylish cut. Long, scraggly grey hair just doesn't make it. You don't want to look grey and old. You want to look grey and chic.

## CHOOSING THE RIGHT STYLE

Your hairstyle says much about you. You tell the world whether you're casual, conservative, sophisticated, or avant-garde by your hairstyle. Sometimes you even tell your age. The woman who still wears a hairstyle that was popular in the 1950s lets everyone know when she left school!

It's important to stay up to date, have fun with your hair, and be comfortable. I recommend going to a great hair stylist for an initial cut and styling. You may need to go two or three times to get it just right. Tell the stylist about your life-style, how handy you are with a blow dryer or curlers, and any past experiences you've had with hairstyles. Evaluate what you're working with. Is your hair limp or coarse? Does it frizz in humid weather? Do you have hair standing up at the crown that plays havoc with a short cut?

Next, tell the stylist what kind of statement you want to make. Use pictures in magazines to illustrate your ideas. Perhaps you're ready to be more sophisticated, or you're just in the mood to try something new. You owe yourself a spiffy style. If you make a mistake, you can always change it! Hair grows. It's fun to have change, and often it takes only a small change to have a great new style. I recall one client who had a permy 'bubble' cut – O.K., but a touch matronly. The stylist simply sculpted the hair closer at the nape of the neck, leaving some longish hair down the neck, and presto – an up-to-date look.

Finally, consider the shape of your face. I find face shape charts to be frustrating and mostly unhelpful. Most faces don't fit them anyway. A rule of thumb is to form your hair to balance the narrow or wide spots and follow the lines of your face.

### Balance

If your face is narrow, fill in the sides with a fuller hairstyle. If your forehead is extremely high, fill it in with some hair – a few wisps, an off-centre parting with some hair falling across the side of the forehead, or full-fledged fringe. If your face is extra wide, sculpt some hair across the wide spots and don't have the style too full.

*Wrong: Old-style 'bubble'.*     *Right: Up-to-date look.*

If you have a prominent feature, such as a large nose or a square jaw, flatter the feature rather than try to cover it up. Balance a prominent nose with fullness at the back of the head – a wedge cut, fluffy layers, short full curls, or a chignon, for example. A long, pointed chin looks great with a haircut that is full and rounded, ending at the chin. A double chin is helped by shortish hair that sweeps upwards and outwards. A small chin is flattered by height at the crown, with the length ending either above or well below the chin line. Flatter a square jaw by exposing it with hair swept back at the temples, and a short cut feathering down the neck, or a longer, angled cut ending below the chin. Don't wear a horizontal fringe or have a horizontal cut ending right at the jawline. A square jaw can be balanced by an asymmetrical haircut, exposing the jaw on one side.

Take the size of your head into consideration, too. If your head is small for your body, have a fuller style. For a large head, choose less fullness.

## Line

The lines of your face give you an automatic direction for your hair. If you have sharp cheekbones and chin, choose a sharp, crisp cut. That's you! The cut can range from severe to slightly curvy, but don't try to change your natural style and 'soften' your angles with a limp

*Wrong: Soft, limp hairstyle detracts from angular face*

*Right: Angular hairstyle complements angular face.*

hairdo. If you have a rounded face, choose a style that has curls or curves, or sweep your hair off your face loosely, rather than tautly. If you have angles, but they're not sharp, you have more flexibility with styles. You can go with either soft, straight lines or curved lines. Very curly hair is best on small to medium-size faces with no sharp features.

Have fun with your features. Don't try to hide them. Go with them rather than against them. Your hair will be not only flattering but also a mark of your self-confidence. Let your hair and your hairstyle show off your personality!

# CHAPTER 16

# FRAGRANCE

MANY women tell me they don't feel completely dressed without scent. Indeed, scent is the finishing touch in completing the image you have carefully created with your make-up and your wardrobe. Not applying your scent is like painting a beautiful picture and neglecting to frame it.

Your season gives you the perfect guidelines for finding that special fragrance that will be your trademark, or for acquiring a wardrobe of fragrances to reflect your every mood. Women of the same season tend to have similar pigmentation and oil content in their skin, and these factors affect how a perfume will react on you. Haven't you ever noticed that a scent you admired on someone else just didn't work on you?

In addition, scent evokes colour. Master perfumers, those talented artists who design the perfumes that become our heart's desire, use colours to describe the mood and make-up of their creation. A fresh, outdoorsy scent is green and yellow. An exotic Oriental fragrance is red and black. Romantic, sweet scents are violet, pink, pastel, and soft white, while rich, sensual fragrances might be fiery red, orange, and gold. Often the colours on the package or perfume bottle denote the mood of the fragrance inside.

I spent two years researching and designing our four Colour Me

Beautiful fragrances. I grew to love the whole concept of fragrance because it appeals to all our senses. The individual scents that go into a fragrance are called 'notes', just as in music. Flavour is represented through the smell of cinnamon, spice, vanilla, and fruity additions. Sight is conjured in our memory through the scents of woods, greenery, and, of course, flowers. Fragrance embodies our total spirit through smell, sound, sight, touch, taste, and, of course, imagination.

In shopping for scent, bear in mind that the 'notes' take time to evolve. The top note is the scent you smell first, when you apply perfume to your skin, creating your first impression. Top notes are volatile and tend to fade quickly. Middle notes begin to appear within a few minutes after application, blending with the top notes. The final notes emerge during the 'dry down' phase of the scent, and these linger several hours after the scent has been applied. The final notes are the main body of a fragrance. To properly evaluate a fragrance, you need to wear it at least one hour, so its full orchestration can appear.

To create the Colour Me Beautiful scents, I worked with a different master perfumer for each season's perfume, so the artist would give his full attention and energy to his creation. We had panels of Winters, Autumns, Summers, and Springs, and our Colour Me Beautiful consultants tested our fragrances at our conventions and in their studios and boutiques. We refined our scents until they were perfect, capturing the essence of each season's woman. Now I can tell a woman's season with my eyes closed – by her perfume!

Your favourite signature scent will most likely come from your own season's array of fragrances, but try on some of the other fragrances as well and see how they react on you. Sometimes we want a different mood or personality. Although I am a Winter, there are days when I feel like a cheeky Spring, a soft romantic Summer, or a warm and fiery Autumn.

## *WINTER*

The Winter woman, with her darker, more dramatic looks and deeper skin tone, wears Oriental scents beautifully. Warmth and mystery best describe the Oriental fragrance family. Orientals are a mélange of rich notes of musk and amber, lush woody notes of sandalwood and patchouli, embellished by sensuous vanilla or exotic fruits.

In designing 'Winter', I wanted to create a mysterious impression. This Oriental fragrance begins with intoxicating top notes of mandarin, spearmint, neroli (citrus), and ylang-ylang. Its unusual and refreshing topnotes are joined by midnotes of jasmine and sensuous rose, with the dry down phase revealing the distinctive notes of vanilla, olibanum, and moss. It's light enough for day, sexy enough for evening. I love it.

In addition to the Colour Me Beautiful fragrance, 'Winter', other favourite winter fragrances are:

Aromatics Elixir, by Clinique

Obsession, by Calvin Klein

Byzance, by Roches

Paloma, by Paloma Piccaso

Magie Noire, by Lancôme

Shalimar, by Guerlain

# SUMMER

The soft, romantic femininity of the Summer woman is best represented by flowery, aldehydic scents. Aldehydes, which create the illusion of pure oxygen (ozone), add sparkle and volume to flowery notes. The ozone effect is not unlike the wonderful aroma that permeates the air in a mountain forest. Beautifully interpreted in 1921 by Chanel No. 5, the flowery aldehydic family is the foundation of many creations, all of which radiate elegance and femininity.

The 'Summer' fragrance by Colour Me Beautiful starts with a delicate bouquet of narcissus and aldehyde, soon surrounded by intimate and sensual florals of rose, jonquil, and marigold, crescendoing into the magical notes of heliotrope, amber, and a touch of vanilla, which adds a powdery note throughout. Summer, to me, describes beauty through and through.

In addition to the Colour Me Beautiful fragrance, 'Summer', other favourite summer perfumes are:

Anaïs Anaïs, by Cacharel

Private Collection, by Estée Lauder

Chanel No. 5, by Chanel

Chanel No. 19, by Chanel

Rive Gauche, by Yves Saint Laurent

Joy, by Patou

Hermes, by Hermes

Le Jardin, by Max Factor

## AUTUMN

A fragrance that marries the delicate florals and rich semi-Oriental families perfectly portrays the Autumn woman, with her combination of warm femininity and tactile sensuality. Semi-Oriental perfume often presents spicy, woody, and musky notes, the family of scents that is sophisticated and opulent.

For 'Autumn' we created a luxurious combination of rare florals. The notes begin with iris and ylang-ylang, enhanced by midnotes of muguet, tagette, and sage clary. Exotic notes of sandalwood, vetiver bourbon, and rich moss complete this magnificent fragrance. It's spicy, woody, and sensual – so Autumn.

In addition to the Colour Me Beautiful fragrance, 'Autumn', other favourite autumn fragrances are:

| | |
|---|---|
| Coco, by Chanel | Opium, by Yves Saint Laurent |
| Cabochard, by Grès | Poison, by Dior |
| Cachet, by Prince Matchabelli | Youth Dew, by Estée Lauder |

## SPRING

The Spring woman is delicate but sensuous, and intensely feminine. She is perfect in a flowery composition that blends different floral scents, subtly combined with green, fruity, spicy, or woody notes. Her fair skin demands a scent that is not too heavy, but her fragrance must nonetheless have presence.

For 'Spring' I wanted to create a tender, yet passionate fragrance. Its first impression is of jasmine and honey, leading into essences of hyacinth, honeysuckle, and lily-of-the-valley, laced by warm, sensuous notes of musk, vetiver and soft amber. Does that sound like you, Spring?

In addition to the Colour Me Beautiful fragrance, 'Spring', other favourite spring perfumes are:

| | |
|---|---|
| Alliage, by Estée Lauder | L'Air Du Temps, by Nina Ricci |
| Charlie, by Revlon | Paris, by Yves Saint Laurent |
| Colours, by Benetton | White Linen, by Estée Lauder |
| Fidji, by Guy La Roche | Wind Song, by Prince Matchabelli |
| Giorgio, by Giorgio | Ysatis, by Givenchy |

## CHOOSING THE RIGHT FORMULA

Fragrance comes in different concentrations. The more oil and less alcohol, the richer and longer-lasting the scent. *Perfume* has the highest concentration of oil and is by far the most expensive. Next comes *eau de parfum* with a fairly high proportion of oil, *eau du toilette*, and then *cologne*, with the least amount of oil and the most alcohol. A woman with dry skin will not have good luck with her scent lasting if she is only using cologne, because neither her skin nor the fragrance has much oil to help the scent linger. She is better off wearing eau de parfum or perfume if she wants her fragrance to stay on all day – or evening.

Fragrance is also available in other forms. Whichever scent you choose, there is more to applying it than simply spraying it on. Here are ways to apply a fragrance so that you will be surrounded, but not smothered, by it all day.

**Bath Products:** Bath products come in many forms: shower and bath gel or mousse, milk bath, bubble bath, and either a bar or cream soap. They all very gently cleanse and/or soften your skin while lightly scenting it.

**After-bath Products:** Scented creams, lotions, and powders are great for after the bath. These pamper your body while lightly scenting it. Apply one of the moisturising products first, then lightly dust with scented powder between and under the breasts, under the arms, and anywhere moisture may collect.

**Light Fragrance Application:** Eau de toilette or parfum or cologne spray. To apply these properly, you should still be unclothed. Spray your fragrance above and slightly in front of you, and walk through the 'cloud' of fragrance. Spraying it behind you next, simply back into the fragrance. Your body will be lightly dusted with fragrance, but not overpowered by it.

**Perfume:** By now, you are very lightly scented from head to toe with your chosen fragrance. Now for the crowning touch, the real thing! Nothing else smells quite like perfume. Dab a tiny bit on several of your pulse points – in the soft spots just behind your earlobes, on either side of your throat, on the back of your neck, between your breasts, inside your wrists, in the crooks of your arms, behind your knees, and on the insides of your ankles.

**Refreshing Your Scent:** Perhaps at midday, and certainly again before you go out in the evening, you will want to refresh your scent. Dabbing more perfume on your pulse points will bring your fragrance alive again. Keep a bottle or jar of scented lotion in your desk drawer, and massage some well into your hands just before you go out of the door. You never know who is going to kiss your hand!

## FRAGRANCE DON'TS

As lovely as fragrance is, there are a few 'don'ts' to remember.

• Do not spray directly onto your clothing. The oils and alcohol will damage your garment, and the scent never smells as lovely on clothing as on you.
• Do not apply a fragrance on bare skin before sunbathing. It can cause pigment discolouration of the skin.
• Do not wear too much. You want people to notice you first, not your perfume.
• Wear a lighter concentration of your fragrance, or a lighter fragrance, during the summer. Heat intensifies a fragrance.
• Store your perfume in a reasonably cool environment.
• Don't apply perfume with the stopper of your perfume bottle. You risk bringing oils and bacteria from your skin back into the bottle.

## ALLERGIES

I can hear some of you: 'I love fragrance, but it makes me sneeze. How can I wear it?' First, use perfume instead of lighter concentrations, as it has no propellant and less alcohol, both of which can cause sneezing (and even headaches). Apply it to the back of your neck, shoulders, and knees only, so it won't always be right under your nose. If you still have a problem, try a different scent. You may be allergic to one of the synthetic or natural oils present in one fragrance but not another. If you have a problem with allergies to perfume, sometimes just skipping it during allergy season when pollen counts are high will help.

Wearing fragrance is extremely personal, because the same scent will never smell exactly the same on two people. You may want to be known for your signature fragrance or you may want variety, with different scents for different moods or occasions. Whatever your choice, your personal fragrance statement will assure you of creating positive memories of you wherever you go.

# INNER BEAUTY

KNOWING we look wonderful on the outside has the positive effect of making us feel beautiful on the inside as well. Wearing our colours, make-up, and an up-to-date hairstyle can produce a mini-miracle in increased self-esteem.

I'm sure you have seen a transformation in either yourself or a friend who has 'found her colours'. With her newfound self-confidence, she radiates good feelings about herself. Perhaps she has made major life changes as a result: changed careers, got a promotion, got married or unmarried, or taken action towards accomplishing a goal. At the very least, she is simply happier, and that happiness spreads to everyone around her.

I believe that inner beauty comes from making the most of our God-given gifts. By becoming our best and using our talents we achieve peace and satisfaction. With increased confidence in ourselves, we often uncover some of our hidden talents because we try things we were afraid to try before.

Whenever I give a speech on personal 'success' or using our gifts, invariably several women come up to me afterwards to tell me of goals they have buried. One woman gave her 'testimonial' to the whole audience. She said she'd always wanted to take singing lessons. She was waiting until her children grew up – but twenty years is a long time to wait. She told us that once she began to feel 'beautiful', she started thinking more of herself in other ways, and decided to start singing now. She had just sung a solo in her community theatre group and was radiant with self-esteem. Everyone clapped vigorously when she finished her story. We can all identify with buried fantasies!

I hope you will use the tools you have learned in this book to look beautiful on the outside, feel wonderful on the inside, and become truly excited about yourself and your personal gifts. The physical and spiritual parts of ourselves taken together make such a beautiful whole person. Let your outer beauty brighten your life and your inner beauty radiate to all those around you.

## COSMETICS, ACCESSORIES, FABRIC SWATCHES

Now that you know your season, write to us for a free catalogue of products to help you get your look together.

## FINDING OR BECOMING AN IMAGE CONSULTANT

If you want help in determining your season, ask us for the name of the consultant nearest to you and details on their range of cosmetics.

If you would like to become a consultant yourself, there are opportunities available for qualified applicants.

For more details, write or telephone

**CMB**

COLOR ME BEAUTIFUL

Freepost
London SW8 3NS

Telephone: 071-627 5211
Fax: 071-627 5680

# INDEX

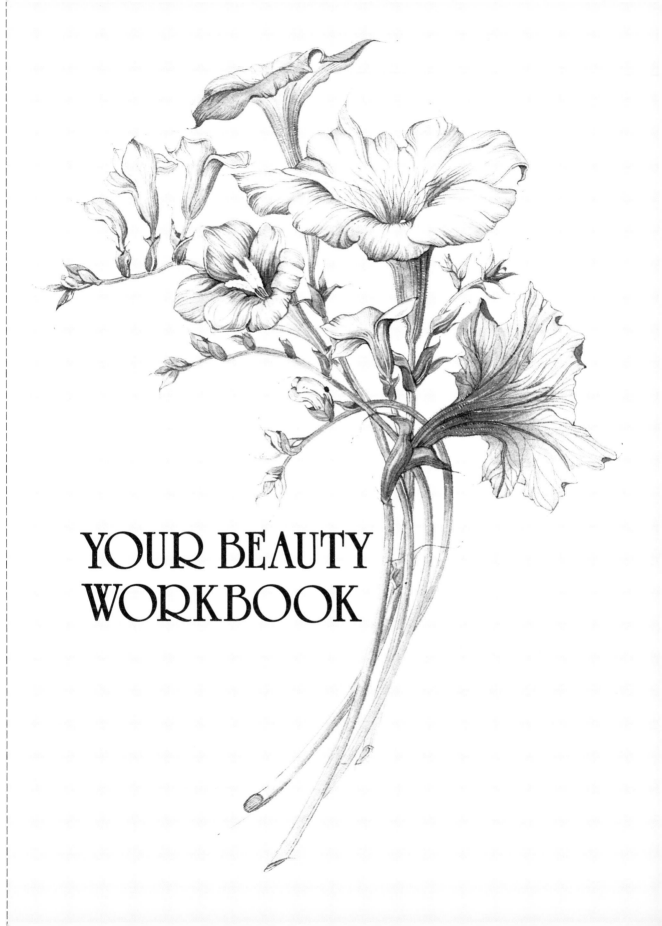

# YOUR BEAUTY
# WORKBOOK

The following charts are designed so you can cut them out of the book, staple the pages together at the top, and make a 'flip' chart to use as a step-by-step guide as you put on your make-up.

Feel free to place the Concealer Chart ahead of the Foundation Chart, if you prefer that order.

Happy make-up!

# SKIN CARE

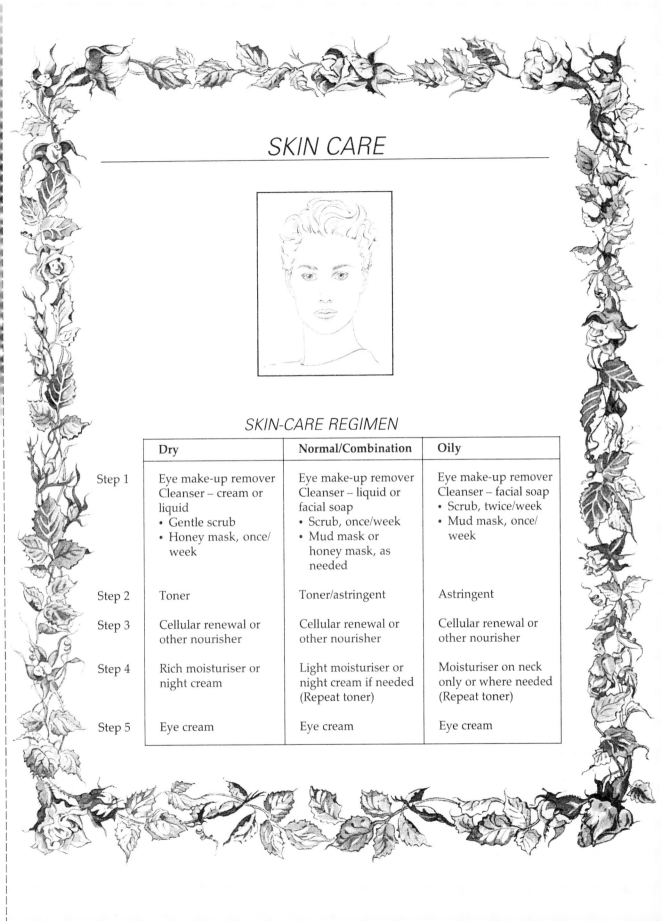

## SKIN-CARE REGIMEN

|        | Dry | Normal/Combination | Oily |
|--------|-----|---------------------|------|
| Step 1 | Eye make-up remover<br>Cleanser – cream or liquid<br>• Gentle scrub<br>• Honey mask, once/week | Eye make-up remover<br>Cleanser – liquid or facial soap<br>• Scrub, once/week<br>• Mud mask or honey mask, as needed | Eye make-up remover<br>Cleanser – facial soap<br>• Scrub, twice/week<br>• Mud mask, once/week |
| Step 2 | Toner | Toner/astringent | Astringent |
| Step 3 | Cellular renewal or other nourisher | Cellular renewal or other nourisher | Cellular renewal or other nourisher |
| Step 4 | Rich moisturiser or night cream | Light moisturiser or night cream if needed (Repeat toner) | Moisturiser on neck only or where needed (Repeat toner) |
| Step 5 | Eye cream | Eye cream | Eye cream |

# FOUNDATION

## WATER OR OIL BASE

Dot on make-up using corner of sponge. Blend with sponge, using downward and outward strokes. Be sure to cover eye, lip and area around nose. Blend carefully at jawline.

## OIL-FREE

Stipple on and feather with fingers to blend, using downward and outward strokes. Avoid eye area. Let dry. 'Buff' with a dry cosmetic sponge. Apply oil-base foundation to eye and lip areas.

*EYE SHADOW BASE:* You can apply eye shadow base instead of foundation to brow and lid area. Dot and blend.

*TIP:* Colour adjuster: Before applying foundation, feather green colour adjuster over ruddy areas, lavender adjuster over sallow cheeks, forehead, chin. Let dry. Follow with foundation.

# CONCEALER

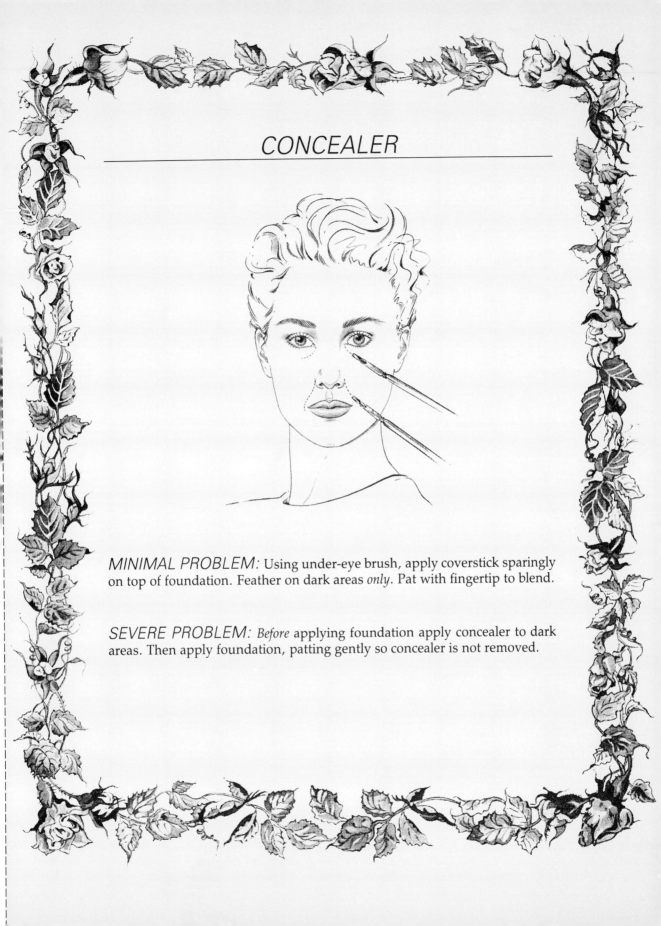

**MINIMAL PROBLEM:** Using under-eye brush, apply coverstick sparingly on top of foundation. Feather on dark areas *only*. Pat with fingertip to blend.

**SEVERE PROBLEM:** *Before* applying foundation apply concealer to dark areas. Then apply foundation, patting gently so concealer is not removed.

# POWDER

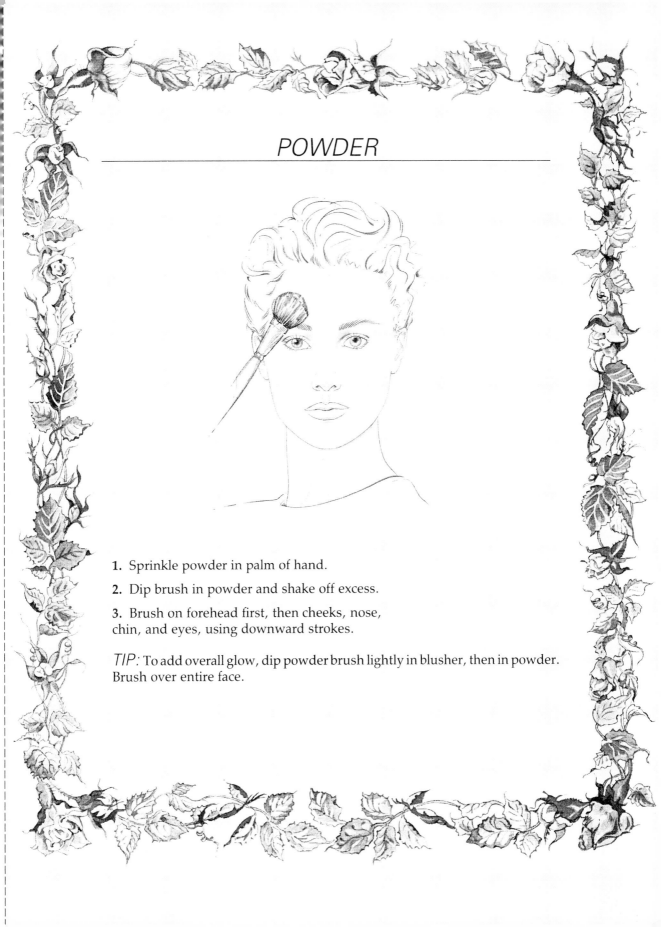

1. Sprinkle powder in palm of hand.

2. Dip brush in powder and shake off excess.

3. Brush on forehead first, then cheeks, nose, chin, and eyes, using downward strokes.

*TIP:* To add overall glow, dip powder brush lightly in blusher, then in powder. Brush over entire face.

# BLUSHER

**1.** Apply blusher along cheekbone, starting right under outer edge of iris, feathering into hairline at top of ear. Do not cover top of cheekbone or go below hollow of cheek.

**2.** Blend edges with contour brush.

## NARROW FACE

Apply blusher from outer edge of eye, blending back (not up) towards centre of ear.

## WIDE FACE

To slim face, bring blusher slightly further forwards and slightly lower, with sharper upward angle towards top of ear.

# EYELINER

### LITTLE OR NO LID SHOWING

Line entire lower lid and outer third of upper lid. Use this technique if no lid shows whether your brow is large or small. Blend to soften.

### PROPORTIONED: LID AND BROW ARE APPROXIMATELY EQUAL

Line outer half of upper and lower lids, feathering edges towards nose so the line doesn't end abruptly. Blend liner to soften.

### PROMINENT LID, SMALL BROW AREA

Line entire upper lid and outer third of lower lid, feathering lower edge so it doesn't end abruptly.

Blend and 'smudge' edges with a clean eye sponge or under-eye brush.

# EYE SHADOW

**1. HIGHLIGHTER:** With your eye sponge, apply a highlighter to entire area, from lashes to brow.

**2. SHADOW COLOUR: OUTER LID:** Using your eye contour brush, apply contour shade to outer third of lid.

### 3. SHADOW COLOUR: ORBITAL BONE

**1.** *Proportioned: Lid and brow area approximately equal.*
Apply contour shadow above the crease, from outer eye to inner, concentrating most of the colour on the outer two thirds of the orbital bone. Blend towards the brow. Apply a pale uplifter colour to the inner two thirds of your lid. Blend. If your lid shows a lot, use a soft neutral, not a lighter bright colour.

**2.** *Little or no lid showing; more brow area.*
Apply contour shadow to orbital bone in a half-circular shape, raising shadow higher towards brow in the centre. Blend upwards and outwards towards brow. Place a dot of uplifter on lid just above iris. Blend slightly.

**3.** *Little or no lid showing; small brow area.*
Apply a pale colour on the entire area from your crease to your brow. Sweep a little of the darker shadow from the outer corner of your lid up towards the end of your eyebrow. Dot uplifter on lid.

**4.** *Prominent lid; small brow area.*
Apply a light shadow on bone above crease, blending it up towards brow. Apply a medium neutral shadow on inner two thirds of lid. Blend. Now brush a little of the darker eye shadow from the outer corner of your lid up towards the end of your eyebrow.

*TIP:* If eye shadow seems too dark, blend entire area with contour brush, stroking upwards; dust with translucent powder.

# MASCARA

1. Apply mascara to upper lashes.

2. Apply to lower lashes.

3. Comb lashes to separate.

4. Let dry.

5. Dust lightly with translucent powder.

6. Repeat.

# EYEBROWS

## 1. SHAPE:

With your brow/lash brush, brush brows upwards and then smooth outwards.

## 2. BROW DEFINER:

Using the same boundaries you use for plucking your brows, feather in pencil or brow powder to fill in length or bare spots.

# LIPSTICK

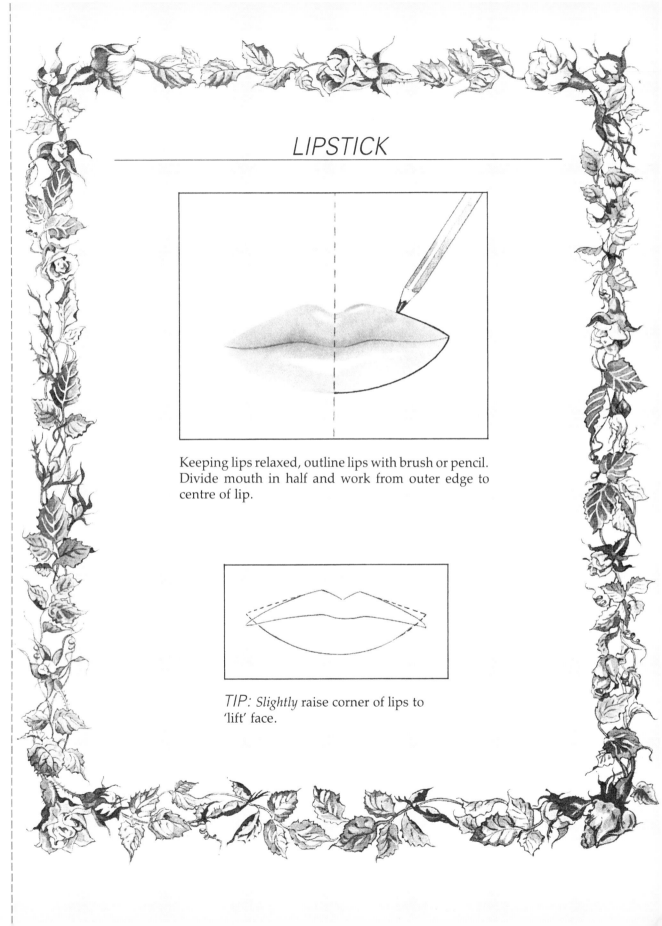

Keeping lips relaxed, outline lips with brush or pencil. Divide mouth in half and work from outer edge to centre of lip.

*TIP: Slightly* raise corner of lips to 'lift' face.

# WINTER MAKE-UP WARDROBE CHART

| Clothing Colour | Lipstick | Blusher | Eye Shadows | |
| | | | Highlighter | Contour Colours |
|---|---|---|---|---|
| All Pinks<br>Magenta<br>Royal Purple<br>Icy Violet | | | | |
| True Red<br>Blue-Red | | | | |
| Fuchsia | | | | |
| Bright Burgundy<br>Vivid Cranberry | | | | |
| Lemon Yellow<br>Icy Yellow | | | | |
| Bright Periwinkle<br>  Blue<br>Royal Blue<br>True Blue<br>Icy Blue | | | | |
| Hot Turquoise<br>Chinese Blue<br>Clear Teal<br>Bright Emerald Turquoise<br>Icy Aqua | | | | |
| Light True Green<br>True Green<br>Emerald Green<br>Pine Green<br>Icy Green | | | | |
| Black<br>White<br>Navy<br>All Greys | | | | |
| Black Brown<br>Taupe | | | | |

# SUMMER MAKE-UP WARDROBE CHART

| Clothing Colour | Lipstick | Blusher | Eye Shadows | |
|---|---|---|---|---|
| | | | Highlighter | Contour Colours |
| All Pinks<br>All Roses<br>Lavender<br>Orchid<br>Medium Violet | | | | |
| Watermelon Red<br>Blue-Red | | | | |
| Soft Fuchsia | | | | |
| Plum<br>All Mauves<br>Raspberry<br>Burgundy/<br>  Maroon | | | | |
| Light Lemon<br>Yellow | | | | |
| Powder Blue<br>Sky Blue<br>Cadet Blue<br>Medium Blue<br>Periwinkle Blue | | | | |
| All Aquas<br>Soft Teal | | | | |
| All Blue Green<br>Spruce Green | | | | |
| Greyed Navy<br>Greyed Blue<br>Light Blue-Grey<br>Charcoal Blue-<br>  Grey | | | | |
| Soft White<br>Rose Beige<br>Rose Brown<br>Cocoa | | | | |

# AUTUMN MAKE-UP WARDROBE CHART

| Clothing Colour | Lipstick | Blusher | Eye Shadows | |
|---|---|---|---|---|
| | | | Highlighter | Contour Colours |
| Orange-Red/Bittersweet<br>Dark Tomato Red | | | | |
| Brown Burgundy<br>Mahogany | | | | |
| All Peaches/Apricots | | | | |
| Orange/Pumpkin<br>Terracotta<br>Rust | | | | |
| Light Gold/Buff Gold<br>Golden Yellow<br>Mustard | | | | |
| Purple<br>Aubergine/Eggplant | | | | |
| Salmon Pink<br>Salmon | | | | |
| Teal Blue<br>Turquoise<br>Jade Green | | | | |
| All Periwinkle Blues | | | | |
| Bright Yellow-Green<br>Forest Green<br>Olive Green<br>Moss Green<br>Greyed Green | | | | |
| Oyster White<br>Warm Beige<br>Khaki/Tan<br>Camel<br>Coffee Brown<br>Dark Brown/Charcoal<br>Medium Warm Bronze<br>Warm Grey/Pewter | | | | |
| Marine Navy | | | | |

# SPRING MAKE-UP WARDROBE CHART

| Clothing Colour | Lipstick | Blusher | Eye Shadows | |
| | | | Highlighter | Contour Colours |
|---|---|---|---|---|
| Warm Pastel Pink<br>Coral Pink<br>Clear Bright Warm Pink<br>Medium Violet | | | | |
| Clear Salmon | | | | |
| Bright Coral | | | | |
| All Peaches/Apricots<br>Light Orange | | | | |
| Orange-Red<br>Clear Bright Red | | | | |
| Buff<br>Light Clear Gold<br>Bright Golden Yellow | | | | |
| All Yellow-Greens<br>Light True Green | | | | |
| All Periwinkle Blues<br>Light True Blue<br>Medium Blue | | | | |
| All Aquas<br>Emerald Turquoise<br>Light Teal Blue | | | | |
| Ivory<br>Light Warm Beige<br>Camel/Tan<br>Medium Golden Brown<br>Chocolate Brown | | | | |
| Light Warm Grey<br>Medium Warm Grey<br>Light Clear Navy<br>Clear Bright Navy | | | | |

## COSMETICS, ACCESSORIES, FABRIC SWATCHES

Now that you know your season, write to us for a free catalogue of products to help you get your look together.

## FINDING OR BECOMING AN IMAGE CONSULTANT

If you want help in determining your season, ask us for the name of the consultant nearest to you and details on their range of cosmetics.

If you would like to become a consultant yourself, there are opportunities available for qualified applicants.

For more details, write or telephone

# CMB
COLOR ME BEAUTIFUL

Freepost
London SW8 3NS

Telephone: 071-627 5211
Fax: 071-627 5680